W9-DEQ-819

ERNAN McMULLIN

editor

Prentice-Hall Fundamentals of Logic Series

METHODS
OF
NATURAL
SCIENCE:
An Introduction

PRENTICE-HALL INTERNATIONAL, INC., *London*
PRENTICE-HALL OF AUSTRALIA, PTY. LTD., *Sydney*
PRENTICE-HALL OF CANADA, LTD., *Toronto*
PRENTICE-HALL OF INDIA (PRIVATE) LTD., *New Delhi*
PRENTICE-HALL OF JAPAN, INC., *Tokyo*

H. A. NIELSEN

University of Notre Dame

METHODS
OF
NATURAL
SCIENCE:
An Introduction

PRENTICE-HALL, INC., ENGLEWOOD CLIFFS, NEW JERSEY

88535

In Memory of my Father

Editor's Note

Aristotle, it would seem, was the first to write a logic series. He was, it must be conceded, unaware of the fact. Nevertheless, when his successors marked off five of his works as having a special unity of their own and called them the *Organon* (or instrument) of science, they were in effect defining a new discipline which would much later come to be called "logic." This rather unusual origin has left its traces on the subsequent history of logic. The *Organon* was capable of unification in two rather different ways. In dealing with predication and demonstration, many nuances of terminology and division were taken for granted which would find an adequate analysis and justification only in the *Metaphysics*, the *Physics*, and the *De Anima*. Logic, if defined by the entire range of the *Organon*, tended to "precontain" an entire philosophical system, even though its problems were, in fact, treated from its own specific point of view.

An alternative approach was to single out those elements in the *Organon* which would best define logic as *propaedeutic* to philosophy. From the beginning, it was seen that the analysis of the valid forms of inference was the heart of Aristotle's logical effort; second came problems inherent in the use of signs generally and of language in particular. These concerns, although never perhaps quite philosophically "neutral," did not seem to involve an explicit ontology: One can test the validity of a syllogism, as Aristotle was the first to emphasize, in a purely formal way. The great developments that have taken place in logic during the last hundred years were conceived in this spirit.

The authors of this new logic series — all of whom wrote (or are writing) their books while members of the faculty of the University of Notre Dame — on the whole lean toward the second of these approaches to the *Organon*, principally because of the pedagogical clarity it makes possible. The disagreements that prompt the often-heard expostulation, "but *that* isn't logic!" are indeed most often of *pedagogical* origin, since logic is assumed, almost by definition, to be the first liberal arts college course. The question at issue in such disagreements really is: at what point and in what way is philosophy best introduced to the college student?

The series consists — for the moment, at least — of five monographs, each concerned with a well-defined area of contemporary logical research. Its advantages over the more conventional single textbook are manifold. First, each book is written by someone who is in active contact with the latest research in the area covered by the book. It is almost impossible for one person to keep track of the varied domains of logic today. Second, even though the basic elements of introductory logic remain (like Newtonian mechanics) relatively unchanged, the points of emphasis and the modes of organization are seen to alter, and something of the excitement of logic as a growing, living discipline with points of controversy, new developments, a future as well as a past, is communicated to the reader. Third, the authors agree that the starting point of logic is defined by the kinds of language and accepted argument that people actually use. It is no mere calculus, nor is it to be confused with mathematics; it begins from and ends in the discourse of men. But the authors disagree, in practice, about the exact relations between formalism and language, and since their disagreements mirror some very active contemporary controversies on this point, the reader has an unusual opportunity to weigh these different approaches in action, as it were.

Lastly, the series permits exceptionally flexible use by the teacher. Two books deal with formal logic. Otto Bird's *Syllogistic and Its Extensions* provides one of the most complete formal treatments of syllogistic available in English today; for the teacher who wishes to stress Aristotle's original method of inference, this book will display the formal substructure of his method in all its elegance. Milton Fisk's *A Modern Formal Logic* builds up formal logic from the whole range of argument-forms found in ordinary discourse and constructs a powerful and original system of "natural inference" that is in important respects different from the less intuitive "material implication" systems given in the majority of elementary textbooks. Ernan McMullin's *Language and Logic* brings together in a coherent whole some of the central insights in semantics that are scattered from the *De Interpretatione* of Aristotle through later medieval logic to the extensive recent researches of writers like Peirce and Morris. Harry Nielsen's *Method in the Sciences: An Introduction* provides a general introduction to the complex problems of the methodology of the sciences, first discussed by Plato and by Aristotle in his *Posterior Analytics*. And Ivo Thomas' *History of Logic* gives a general outline of the historical development of logic, something that will restore to the subject as a whole a dimension that is notably lacking in most general textbooks. With all of this material at his disposal, the teacher can pick and choose, and thus can construct a course that ought ultimately to bear the stamp of his own personal approach to logic.

Ernan McMullin
Notre Dame, Ind.

Preface

The chapters that follow give to the reader a general idea of the methods of inquiry used in natural science. These methods grow from investigative processes of thought used in the most ordinary domestic forms of inquiry, which can illustrate many of the lessons methodology has to teach. Where reference is made to actual sciences, we can leave to the experts such frontier issues as the status of the latest particle and concern ourselves with the more accessible reaches of science. Within that extensive compass our concern will be with methods as revealed in day-to-day research, or in practice rather than in published results. Also, where method is the topic of discussion, mistakes and failures in the history of science can be just as revealing as the study of completed scientific documents.

The first aim of methodology is to distinguish and describe the ways in which men have learned to wring knowledge out of their surroundings. Second, in line with the traditional aims of logic, methodology treats of the rules, cautions, and economies built into scientific procedures as safeguards against error and wasted effort. We hardly need to be reminded that a discussion of general principles will not replace the years of training needed to make a researcher. Neither will it bring under easy survey the thousands of distinct techniques used in the sciences, which novices in various fields must learn from experienced men. If the reader opens a handbook of bacteriology, for example, he will find detailed instructions on how to isolate, stain, preserve, and classify microorganisms; a field manual of paleontology will tell him how to stake out a fossil bed and apply chemical and physical tools to secure undamaged specimens. This sort of knowledge grows from direct contact with objects in their natural surroundings, and no instruction at the level of logic can substitute for it. At the same time, the techniques described in manuals are instruments in the service of more basic practices: collecting relevant data, generalizing, formulating and testing hypotheses, running experiments, and constructing theories. With these practices go a number of rules and caveats that hold good for any instance, and which methodology as a regular branch of logic proposes to treat systematically.

In the sections on modern methodology the author has taken a number of cues from Charles S. Peirce, the American logician and philosopher whose widely acknowledged contributions to the logic of science can be found in the eight-volume Harvard University Press edition of his *Collected Papers*, edited by Charles Hartshorne, Paul Weiss, and Arthur Burks. On occasion I have found it helpful to consult Peirce's articles—unsigned but recognizably his own to any reader who knows his work—in the *Century Dictionary* (1914). I owe further thanks to Professors Ernan McMullin and Otto Bird of Notre Dame University for valuable suggestions.

H. A. NIELSEN
Notre Dame, Ind.

Contents

1

Basic
Types
of
Reasoning

§1   One Kind of Deductive Reasoning

Mathematics and formal logic employ a variety of formulas that enable their users to move from something laid down or accepted (a premiss) to something else (a conclusion) that is said necessarily to follow. Other volumes in this series describe certain formulas in this pattern and the kinds of ordering or systematizing they permit.[1] Reasonings that employ such formulas are called *deductive* and occur in such a variety that it is difficult fully to catalog even those used within a single general discipline such as mathematics. Our primary concern in this book is to discuss another sort of reasoning, sometimes called *inductive* or *experimental*, in which the bond between premisses, or data, and conclusion is *not* built into the pattern of reasoning. Instead it is established empirically, that is, by reference to factual experience, in a variety of ways. To heighten the contrast between these basic types of reasoning, it will be helpful to consider first an example of deduction.

Plane geometry is a branch of mathematics with which most readers have had some contact. An example taken from geometry will serve as a reminder of some features of deductive reasoning that contrast importantly with features of experimental reasoning.

First, construct a square *ABCD*. Then, by drawing two straight lines within the square and parallel to each of two adjacent sides, divide the square into two unequal squares and two equal rectangles. Draw a diagonal in each of the two rectangles, so as to make four equal right triangles. Now, in a new square the same size as the original, *EFGH*, distribute the four right triangles inside the periphery so that each right angle coincides with one of the four corners of *EFGH*. The

---

[1] Cf. M. Fisk, *A Modern Formal Logic* (1964), and O. Bird, *Syllogistic and Its Extensions* (1964).

resulting square-within-a-square *efgh* is seen to enclose an area equal to that of the two unequal squares in *ABCD*. But *efgh* is built on the hypotenuse of a right triangle, whereas the two unequal squares in *ABCD* are built on the shorter sides of the same right triangle. Therefore a square on the hypotenuse of a right triangle encloses an area equal to the sum of the squares on its shorter sides.

With the help of diagrams drawn by the reader this demonstration runs along easily enough, although he will notice that several subordinate steps are omitted. We did not stop to prove that *efgh* is a square or to cite our justification for calling *EFGH* the same size as *ABCD*. However, accepting the whole series of steps as an unpolished bit of geometry, we can go on to notice a number of points about procedure in a formal science. First of all, the squares and triangles we are dealing with are *ideal* or *hypothetical* entities. The properties they possess are limited to (a) those that appear in the definition of the figure or in the specifications for constructing it and (b) those that can be derived from (a) with the aid of postulates and other theorems of the system. Where the properties of an entity depend entirely upon the stipulations of the investigator, or rather the community of investigators, whatever is true of one square or right triangle will be true of any other, if indeed there is any point in distinguishing one and many. Thus the theorem in our example, credited to Pythagoras, could be expressed by saying either *"The* right triangle has as one of its properties . . ."* or, more conventionally, "For *any* right triangle, the square of the hypotenuse equals . . . ." One can view a theorem in geometry either as a generalization about a plurality or as a singular statement about a particular formula for juxtaposing lines. It is important to keep in mind that the kind of generalizing we find in a theorem dealing with *all* right triangles is not at all like the kind we express in saying that all known felines are carnivores. The certainty and universality we associate with formal sciences derive from the fact that triangles cannot change as cats can; the former cannot elude us in bush country as can some warier species of cat. Whatever man can put together hypothetically (such as triangles), by means of thought, can be kept before his mind for further analysis without fear of its mutating suddenly to produce exceptions. Such concerns will come up presently in connection with empirical generalizing.

If the triangles and other figures analyzed by the geometer exist by stipulation, or in other words by the agreement of geometers on the manner of constructing them, where are the geometer's *permissions* grounded? That is, what principles control and limit the operations by which he moves from the minimally defining characteristics of a right triangle to the often surprising and unlooked-for relations expressed in the theorems he proves? The geometer's method, as our example shows, consists in first breaking a prescribed figure into its parts, then rearranging those parts in order to produce a new figure that will highlight a relationship among them, and finally asserting that relationship in the form of a theorem. For geometry and for every other formal science, the principle underlying the increase of knowledge may be expressed in this way: Hypothetical objects (numbers, lines, planes, and so on) admit of being constructed, broken down, and juxtaposed in such a way as to reveal new relationships between wholes or their parts.

§2   Reasoning About Physical Entities

The term *induction* has been used as a catchall for experimental reasonings of every kind. In its compact dictionary definition, inductive reasoning is said to go from the particular to the general, whereas deductive goes from the general to the particular. This brief definition blurs what might be called the broad, natural divisions of experimental reasoning. These include judging from a sample or specimen, formulating and testing a hypothesis, developing a theory to cover a wide field of data, establishing a law or empirical formula, and designing and running a decisive experiment. It is by no means necessary to suppose that these modes of scientific reasoning have a common structure that can be represented by a single logical pattern. Their strength and usefulness to man are derived not from any demonstrative necessity attaching to the logical links between data and conclusions, but from the pains taken by their users to ward off the dangers peculiar to each mode of reasoning. Although there may be some theoretical value in seeking a pattern of likeness in all these modes, our present aims will be better served by emphasizing differences.

When a geometer proves that right triangles have such and such a property, the result is incorporated into the body of geometrical knowledge as a truth affecting any and every right triangle. Although perfect generality of this sort is common in the theorems of mathematics, it is not so easily achieved or so insistently sought after in empirical inquiries. The reasons behind this contrast are worth noticing. First of all, the figures we consider in geometry are hypothetical entities even if certain ones happen to be embodied in natural objects. The properties of, say, a hexagon are limited to those given in or implied by the specifications that humans lay down for constructing one. In this respect a hexagon lacks what Aristotle called a nature, an inner spur that causes it to go its own way or perhaps change without notice and betray our expectations. Fickleness is not among the traits we build into geometric figures. Hence the geometer need not fear that anything of the sort will spoil the generality of a theorem about hexagons. Besides having no independent natures, the figures of geometry have no outer environment to affect them, no neighboring influence that could bend a right angle away from ninety degrees or alter the proportion between the squares of its sides. In working.out proofs, therefore, the geometer has no need to take into account the physical surroundings or the time of day. This is not to deny that one can go wrong in geometry. Going wrong in that context, however, means making a bad step in the proof, assuming too much, or something similar; the error will not derive from the figure's changing suddenly or reacting to something in the room.

When we turn from geometry and other deductive sciences to ask about the basis for safe generalization in the physical domain, two contrasts stand out immediately. First, a serious investigator in the field of medicine or physics cannot afford to treat the things he studies as if they had no existence of their own, no properties apart from those that humans prescribe to them. Second, he must soon come to see them as affected by neighboring things in space. A single example will illustrate both of these principles. Suppose a public health worker wants to determine the bacteria count of reservoir water. He draws samples from various depths, mixes and dilutes them according to a standard procedure, and streaks the mixture on a plate of sterile jelly, which under controlled warmth will nourish colonies of microbes and give him his count. Then, we imagine, he happens to sneeze over the exposed plate. No special training in bacteriology is needed to warn us that he can no longer trust the contaminated culture to tell him much about the reservoir. We can decide the success or failure of a mathematical calculation, on the other hand, without reference to the physical conditions under which it was derived.

We are now in a position to draw an important line between formal or deductive sciences on the one side and experimental or inductive sciences on the other. In pure mathematics the material circumstances under which we arrive at a conclusion do not affect its reliability. In experimental reasonings they do. The sections that follow describe a number of ways in which awareness of this contrast helps take the hazard out of nondeductive inferences.

§3   The Practice of Sampling

We may begin with a type of generalization familiar to everyone: judgments based on sampling. The cook samples her gravy before serving it to see if it needs a dash of spice. The shopper who fears that the berries on top of the box may conceal a poorer grade fingers a few underneath to get a better sample. If we stop to recall a number of such practices, which are so woven into the routine of our lives that we hardly think of them as conforming to a set of rules, the most conspicuous feature of sampling quickly suggests itself: It consists typically in judging the quality of a whole by examining a small quantity.

It is important to notice, however, that this characterization of sampling applies with equal force to hasty and biased generalizations, as in measuring the seriousness of a whole student body by the bad manners of a bumptious few. Our first stab at a definition leaves out, in fact, precisely what concerns us most: the methods by which hazard is systematically reduced in judging from samples. If it is to withstand the criticisms rightly leveled against careless generalizing, then there must be more to sampling than the one common feature we first noted.

At the outset of a typical sampling operation the inquirer wishes first of all to find out something about a collection or quantity. Sampling is not an accidental, unpremeditated encounter with a subclass or small fraction of a quantity, but a purposeful selection or drawing. Reminded of this, we may amend our definition: Sampling consists in examining a small quantity selected in such a way as to reveal approximately the quality of the lot from which it was drawn. The fact that sampling is not passive but involves doing what we can to get a sample that will nearly match its population reminds us that, in any actual case, the question of *how to go about it* must be considered. This question calls to mind a number of options by means of which the sampler can proceed.

First, the quality one is sampling for ought to be specified before the sample is drawn; to borrow Charles S. Peirce's expression, it should be *predesignated*. The easiest way to see the reasonableness of this rule is to conduct a little experiment along lines suggested by Peirce. From the biographical listings in *Webster's Collegiate Dictionary* we might copy out six or eight names of celebrated persons, with their birth and death dates, using a formula that we have no reason to think will prejudice the character of our selection. We choose, let us say, the fourth name listed under every fourth letter of the alphabet, beginning with A:

Abdel-Kader	1807–1883
Ebert, Friedrich	1871–1925
Ibrahim Pasha	1789–1848
McCormick, Cyrus	1809–1884
Quincy, Josiah	1744–1775
Ulpian	170?–228
Young, Brigham	1801–1877

We might call this a *random* selection in one sense of the word, for the names were drawn quite blindly according to a formula chosen arbitrarily. But strictly speaking we have no right to regard it as a sample; we have not established beforehand the quality we wish to sample for. If we treat this selection as a sample, that is, as a fair cross section of famous persons, we introduce serious risk of error in any conclusions we might draw.

To illustrate, someone noticing the last name in the list might conclude that one out of every seven famous persons is a Mormon. Going further, three out of seven are Americans, two out of seven are Moslems. Absences in the list might suggest that the number of famous Frenchmen, Greeks, Orientals, and women is close to zero. Turning to the dates, it would seem that three out of every seven famous persons were born in the first decade of the nineteenth century and that virtually no famous persons die in their sixties.

Some of the conclusions just drawn are affronts to common knowledge, and a little time spent with a biographical dictionary will show that the rest are wildly inaccurate. A reasoner who ignores the rule of predesignation puts himself at the mercy of the accidental aspects of the selection. If we look hard enough at any arbitrary selection from a class, we can find in it features, or peculiar ratios of features, that cannot be safely attributed to the whole class.

It might at first sound extravagant to blame such a flurry of wrong conclusions on the mere failure to predesignate what we are sampling for. For example, if we had set out to determine the percentage of Poles among famous persons, might we not have come up with the same selection and gone wrong despite our pains? It is true, we might agree, that the mere act of saying in advance what we are sampling for would not determine the particular names drawn. However, it might greatly affect the number of names in our sample, our selection of the source, our willingness to depend on a single source, and even our choice of sampling as our method.

The rule of predesignation, then, is part of the concept of sampling, part of what we might call its expanded definition, which now runs as follows: Sampling consists in examining a small quantity out of a lot or batch, with a view to ascertaining the quality of the whole in a certain predesignated respect.

Predesignation is not the only practice employed to minimize error in sampling. Consider two routine illustrations. In the first, a laboratory technician in a dairy must test for the butterfat percentage in a vat containing about one thousand gallons of raw whole milk. Before dipping out a sample he switches on an agitator to mix the milk thoroughly.

In the second, a public health worker is asked to measure the average turbidity of river water in an industrial area. The samples are collected on a weekday, every three hours during a twenty-four-hour period. A quart of water at a time is taken from the river about a half mile downstream from the factory area, a distance in which sewage has had a chance to disperse. The water is taken from both sides of the river at several depths. At the end of the period he shakes the separate quarts to loosen any sediment and pours them into a crock, where they are mixed once more. The technician fills a glass tube with the fresh mixture, inserts it into a photometer, and reads the result against standardized turbidity slides.

In these examples the sampler brings *physical force* to bear upon the materials he is testing. The dairy worker lets a mechanical mixer do the work of homogenizing the batch. The public health worker must go from place to place in a boat to gather his composite sample. It is easy to imagine how far off the result might be if the first man neglected to agitate the milk and ran his test on cream from the top of a settled vat or if the second ran his test on water taken near the outlet of a dye works.

The use of force wherever practicable is a common expedient in sampling. It illustrates, perhaps more convincingly than any other factor, that sampling is not a casual waiting game in which the reasoner judges the quality of a lot by examining a few particulars that happen to catch his eye. Force, however, does not apply in every kind of sampling. Let us imagine a case in which a television survey team sets out to estimate the number of local housewives who watch the morning show *Home Folks*. The human subjects of this survey are separate individuals whose movements fall outside the team's control. The plan, then, is to run a telephone survey. Using a directory that lists thirty thousand home telephones, the team will make three hundred calls. First they make certain that no major public events are scheduled for the two mornings of the survey and that the weather is normal for the season. To pick the names they lay a cardboard scale against the telephone listings and use every hundredth name. If a phone is registered for a business, the caller picks the next name. If no one answers a ring, the result goes in as negative. Busy phones are called again until the party is reached or fails to answer. Each person polled is asked three questions:

1.   What show, if any, are you watching?
2.   If it is *Home Folks*, are you a regular watcher?
3.   If it is not, how often do you watch *Home Folks*?

When the data are in, the percentages of regular and occasional watchers are determined by normal statistical procedures.

In this example physical force has no clear application. Instead, the team must exercise *attention to the immediate circumstances* of their inquiry. Their data must be gathered with forewarning of any unusual circumstances, such as weather that might keep people indoors or civic affairs that might call them away. In more complex kinds of sampling, such as pre-election polls, many more factors must be weighed. A poll on a national scale, sounding out opinion before a presidential election, must take into account the distribution of rich and poor in its sample, regional trends, late-breaking news items, and the breakdown of the "undecided" group in terms of income, race, and religion. Pollsters must also consider the particular issues under debate in an election if the results of a poll are to be kept within normal margins of accuracy.

The point of airing these well-known complications is to remind ourselves of another general practice connected with sampling: The sampler must in many cases lean on his special knowledge of the distribution and stratification of the objects he is sampling. In addition to predesignation, attention to the immediate circumstances, and where possible the use of force, we must bring in the notion of *expertness* if our characterization of sampling is to be complete. Many sampling techniques demand a kind of familiarity with special subjects that comes only with repeated effort and years of experience. Although this fact is at its most striking in political forecasting, where in election years the man with a feeling for subtle currents and straws in the wind finds eager listeners, it is no less important in industry and in the sciences.

Our initial characterization of sampling has been expanded to include a number of concepts which, though we may not find them in a dictionary definition, are essential to a clear understanding of how sampling contributes to the production of safe generalizations. A final expansion of our first definition might be written this way: Sampling consists in examining a small quantity of a whole and judging the quality of the whole in a certain predesignated respect; the drawing of a reliable sample calls for alertness to the immediate surroundings and for the use of physical force, where possible, to aid in getting a sample that will match its source; good results in many kinds of sampling often depend on expert knowledge of the type of thing under study. The importance of keeping all these features in view will become clearer when we consider some treatments that omit one feature or another and thus misrepresent sampling as well as other forms of empirical reasoning.

Closely related to the concept of sample is that of specimen. The terms are sometimes used interchangeably, as when physicians speak of a blood sample or blood specimen. More often a specimen is an individual object prepared and preserved to represent either a species in zoology or botany, or a mass or quantity from which it was collected. A specimen of granite in a mineral collection may be starred as much for its unusual features (its gemstone impurities, for example) as for its representative ones. Generally, however, a specimen is chosen with its type or species in mind. Whether or not a given specimen, say of ore-bearing rock, can be used as a sample to ascertain the general quality of its source depends upon the pains taken to insure its qualitative resemblance to its surroundings when it was collected.

§4 The Rationale of Sampling

Our motive for turning to samples in various situations can be expressed in a few words: economy of time, effort, and money. Putting the same thought more positively, we can see in the practice of letting samples guide us one of the ways in which humans depend on experience. Many logicians and philosophers, reflecting on the fact that we often rely on generalizations that go beyond the immediate data they are based on, have concerned themselves with the rationale of this human behavior. On what grounds, they ask, can we justify such optimism? The things we reason about in geometry and other deductive disciplines must of necessity behave in certain ways, for they have no properties, no existence even, beyond what our specifications confer upon them. In the physical realm, on the other hand, anything can happen. What, then, is the logical bond, the connection, between a generalization ("This batch of milk contains 3 per cent butterfat") and the evidence for it (the butterfat content of a small sample)?

The Scottish philosopher David Hume (1711–1776) gave the problem of induction a generalized modern expression that calls in question the rationale of all varieties of experimental reasoning. In Hume's view the only justification for our depending on experience, say our experience of a sample, is the belief that nature is uniform, that the future will be like the past, or, in the present context, that the rest of any batch will be like the sample. But this belief, he adds, is itself a generalization based on experience and stands as much in need of justifying as does any lesser generalization. Therefore our confidence in knowledge gained from samples rests on a kind of faith, not on reason.

Many philosophers go along with Hume in supposing that a suppressed premiss figures in judging from samples. They represent sampling judgments as follows:

> This bit of milk, drawn from that batch, shows about 3 per cent fat.
> Therefore, the whole batch is about 3 per cent fat.

Looking at this representation, they notice that the premiss not only does not prove its conclusion, but does not even make it probable. This bit of milk may very well have characteristics unlike those of its source. However, if we add a further premiss to this effect: *'Nature is uniform; what is true of the examined part of a physical quantity will be true of the rest'*, then without a doubt we make this representation of sampling look deductive. In effect the added premiss declares the world a permanently safe place for sampling. However, Hume's problem is not solved by merely inserting the added premiss. His point is that its truth must be proved. Efforts to meet his challenge are still going on, since there is no general agreement that any earlier ones have succeeded. Although it would take us off course to explore or even to summarize these efforts, it may be worthwhile to suggest another way of looking at Hume's problem.

How can we justify the practice of depending on samples to yield reliable generalizations? In the light of matters already discussed, an answer suggests itself. The pains we take to get a representative sample are what justify us in this or that particular case. Surely we do not wish to justify careless acts of sampling in the same breath with those in which the sampler makes every effort to secure a representative selection. On the other hand, if we can justify depending on a sample in any particular case by citing the pains we took, no further justification seems needed. This is ordinarily as far as our everyday thinking goes on the subject of justification. But what then becomes of Hume's problem? Its application to sampling appears to fade away entirely.

Why do philosophers seem to see a need for justifying sampling? The apparent need for justification, we could suggest, lies not in the actual practice of sampling but in a certain way of representing it, namely, by means of an *argument-form* such as the syllogism:

> The examined part of the class M is n per cent P.
> Therefore the whole class M is n per cent P.

The assertion of all such formulas is that they capture everything essential to the operation of sampling, everything the sampler depends upon for good results. In the branch of deductive logic called *syllogistic*, we may recall, formulas of a similar kind prove useful and do in fact capture the essence of the arguments they represent. For example, the schema

> All M is P,
> All S is M,
> Therefore All S is P

preserves everything the reasoner requires to meet the conditions of formal validity. Provided he substitutes correctly for *S, M,* and *P,* he will never be led from true premises to a false conclusion. It can be tempting to imagine that a schema constructed along similar lines will do the same for inductive reasoning. Here, however, it will be helpful to remember the principle mentioned in § 2. The reliability of empirical generalizations, as opposed to those in mathematics, depends upon the physical circumstances under which the inquirer obtains his data. It is therefore essential that any full and faithful representation of actual sampling mention the pains that must be taken in actual sampling situations. No formula of the sort we have just been considering can guide the sampler's steps or make him a competent sampler. It must leave out precisely what the inquirer depends upon for good results: physical techniques for making the sample match its source as nearly as possible.

Some logicians who write about induction might protest that the need to justify sampling goes deeper than these remarks have suggested and is not to be thought of as arising from a misleading way of representing judgments from samples. "Represent them in any way you wish," someone might say. "Still, no matter how much detail you go into about taking pains, you will find that the logical relation between your conclusion and the evidence for it will be too weak to justify people's well-known confidence in sampling. A mere reference to taking pains cannot knock out the possibility of the sampler's getting a disastrously wrong result." In reply we might ask the speaker what kind of possibility he thinks is a threat to sampling. One kind that samplers are concerned about, as we have seen, is the kind that can be forestalled by taking precautions of various sorts, using force sometimes, and keeping watch over the surroundings. When something goes wrong and a sample proves to be misleading, methods of sampling can be adapted to allow for whatever changed the situation. This kind, which we may for convenience call the *physical* possibility of getting disastrous results, can hardly be what our objector has in mind, for it is a threat that samplers methodically and often routinely guard against.

Another kind of possibility is associated with calculations, syllogism, and deduction generally. We call it *logical* possibility, and logicians make use of it in explaining notions such as *formal validity* and *proof.* Imagine this syllogism:

> Every cup of milk I tasted was sweet.
> Every cup of milk I tasted came from that pasteurizer.
> Therefore, every cup of milk in that pasteurizer is sweet.

It would be appropriate for a logician to point out that this argument is formally invalid, even though in a given instance its premisses and conclusion might all happen to be true. "The premisses do not prove the conclusion. Given those premisses, it is still logically possible that the cups you tasted were the only sweet cupfuls in a pasteurizer of sour milk. Someone, perhaps a demon, may have played a trick. Farfetched? Well, remember that proving something in logic means excluding *all* possibilities that might be inconsistent with your conclusion. By failing to distribute your minor term, you failed to do this." These words are common in the study of formal inference and need not be multiplied further. They remind us, however, that logical possibilities are those that threaten the integrity only of deductions.

The logical possibility of getting wrong results, then, poses no threat to the reasonableness of sampling, where of course we are not deducing anything. Accordingly, judging from samples is to be regarded not as a weakened form of deduction, but as a different genus of reasoning altogether, based on a different principle.

These remarks, far from being an attempt to solve Hume's problem, merely suggest that it has no application to sampling. Its presumed applications to other modes of experimental reasoning will be discussed later.

2

The Logic of Explanations

§5 Propounding and Using Hypotheses

When we ask ourselves what it means or what it is like to explain a fact, familiar instances rush to mind. If these happen to come from natural science (for example, modern physics), their authority may tempt us to propose a nutshell definition, such as "Explaining consists in bringing a particular phenomenon under a general law." For certain kinds of explanation this or any first try at an answer may be tolerably accurate. However, when the meaning of a common word is in question, it is usually safer to resist the desire for a one-sentence definition. As we saw in relation to sampling, a good many diverse examples may be needed to ascertain the role of a much used concept. Let us begin by citing a few transparent examples to build upon.

First a domestic example. A housewife goes to the cupboard. In the wrapper of an unopened loaf of bread, bought the day before, she notices a small round hole. The crust has been eaten through, and a few crumbs are scattered nearby. After puzzling for a moment she says, "We have a mouse."

In the second example, a medical one, a young man is helped into a doctor's office. The doctor examines the young man's swollen ankle, injured in a ball game. "It looks to me like a fracture," he says, "but we'll have to take an X ray. It might be just a sprain."

Finally a geological example. In the level Arizona desert near Winslow is a crater with a rim 160 feet high. It spans 4,000 feet and is 600 feet deep. Naturalists investigating the crater report that the most likely explanation is that a meteorite crashed into the spot thousands of years ago.

In each of these examples the inquirer finds his attention drawn to an unlooked-for phenomenon. There are no rules limiting what may

13

strike a person; it may be an irregularity in the routine course of events or a regular occurrence, such as the fact that draining water whirls clockwise north of the equator and counterclockwise south. Once interested, the inquirer entertains ideas that might be reasons for the phenomenon, until one of them stands out as more plausible than its alternatives. This he adopts more or less tentatively as the true hypothesis.

Propounding an explanation is only the first step toward settled knowledge. Even at this initial stage, however, some rules must control the free play of imagination. The supreme rule of explanatory reasoning is that the phenomenon prompting the explanation should be honestly appraised. The fact to be explained must, in other words, be soundly enough established to justify the effort that goes into conceiving and confirming a hypothesis. To illustrate, imagine a hypochondriac, a person who is prey to morbid thoughts about his health. He might attempt self-diagnosis along these lines: "I wonder why I feel so done in this evening. I feel the way Jones looks. Poor Jones with his anemia. Maybe that's it. I have anemia." Here the occasion for a diagnosis (the symptom) is not first brought into clear view to see whether a medical question is involved at all. The hypochondriac permits his anxiety to blur the difference between a clearly manifested symptom, which would indeed call for explaining, and the vaguely out-of-sorts feeling that everyone experiences now and then.

Further violations of the rule of careful appraisal may be found in a number of eccentric pet theories. Arguments that Francis Bacon or someone else wrote the plays attributed to Shakespeare are well-known instances of hypothetical inference based on erroneous assumptions. Such assertions usually begin by insisting that the real author must have had academic training, for example in law, classics, or state protocol, in order to display such familiarity with those matters in his writings. However, if historical records are any indication, Shakespeare's formal education was narrow and limited. Since Shakespeare can hardly qualify as the real author, who wrote those plays and poems? The question seems to call for a hypothesis naming this or that candidate; at least half a dozen have been proposed. The hypothesis that Lord Bacon wrote the plays is occasioned not by any fact definitely indicating Bacon, but rather by a questionable assumption: William of Stratford lacked some qualifications that the real author *must* have had. Given that assumption, the theorist can range through the gallery of Shakespeare's contemporaries, pick out the best qualified man (or woman, as one theorist maintains), and then make an ephemeral mark on the literary world by exhibiting his discovery. When the argument is presented in finished form, it can look deceptively like a sound piece of reasoning.

To assure himself that efforts in behalf of the Baconian or any similar hypothesis are well spent in the service of truth, the inquirer should first make sure that the need for a hypothesis is genuine. Can we be certain that the author of *Hamlet* could not possibly have written it unless his schooling had been that of a nobleman? Some examination of the academic backgrounds of literary giants would show that gifted men can extend their command of language in ways other than formal education.

The sciences are not immune from the temptation to rush forward with a hypothesis before one is genuinely occasioned. Near the end of the nineteenth century the Italian astronomer Giovanni Schiaparelli announced the discovery of a network of nearly straight lines resembling channels (*canali*) on the surface of Mars. Taking up the cry, the American astronomer Percival Lowell and others claimed to have observed a veritable maze of channels, some thousands of miles long and up to fifty miles wide. The problem of accounting for these new observations led inevitably to the hypothesis (in many minds nearly a proof) that the channels were waterways designed for irrigation by intelligent beings. However, when the improved resolving power of modern optical systems failed to reveal a Martian surface laced with straight lines, the excitement died down. Until further evidence bears out the existence of *canali*, the reports of their honest discoverers must be ascribed to optical illusion and eyestrain.

Our three opening examples of hypotheses—the mouse, the fracture, and the meteorite—were all sufficiently occasioned by fact and thus met the first rule of hypothetical reasoning. They also show another characteristic: Each of them admits of being followed up, confirmed, or disconfirmed by later findings. The housewife who thinks a mouse has moved in can take steps that may confirm her suspicion; mice have nests and offspring, leave tracks, and can be caught. An X ray can show for certain that the ankle is cracked. Meteorites leave characteristic residues where they hit. Mice, fractures, and meteorites are, in other words, things one can search for. Finding one of them, under the circumstances described in our examples, means elevating into virtually settled knowledge the hypothesis that first suggested its presence.

§6 Testing Hypotheses

The procedure in testing a hypothesis involves, in the most general terms, summoning to mind and checking out a number of other propositions that would normally be true if the hypothesis itself were true. These predictions, or anticipations of confirming evidence, need not be strictly or formally deducible from the original hypothesis, as some logicians maintain. The housewife, for instance, can look for signs that are usual or natural concomitants of a mouse, even if their presence is not a logically necessary consequence.

The first rule in testing a hypothesis is to test only those propositions that will help settle the question decisively. To see how this rule is sometimes violated, let us go back to the hypochondriac. A normal person who thinks he might have anemia could make an honest and decisive prediction along these lines: "Well, if I have anemia my blood count will be low. The sensible thing to do is to stop at the clinic and have a blood count taken." But suppose someone's thoughts run like this: "Yes, no doubt I have anemia. Come to think of it, my blood looked a little pinkish this morning when I nicked my chin shaving. And now that I look back, I've been feeling the cold more than usual. This is typical of people with pernicious galloping anemia. In the office I need a pick-me-up around four in the afternoon. At mealtimes I can't seem to put away more than one serving of everything. It can't be anything but anemia."

This man does not bother with predictions at all. He merely lets secondary morbid thoughts follow the initial morbid thought. Instead of predictions, they are associations vaguely suggested by the mention of an enfeebling disease. Thus, although the data he recalls have a certain resemblance to evidence, they are brought to bear upon the "hypothesis" in a manner that annuls their usefulness as evidence.

A corollary to our first rule states that the selection of test-propositions should not favor those that are likely to come true whether the hypothesis is correct or not. To illustrate, imagine that a councilman in a small town, driving alone in his automobile, crashes into a pole and dies instantly. The insurance agent reviewing the widow's claim knows that the policy provides for payment of fifty thousand dollars for accidental death but for nothing at all in case of suicide. To avoid the loss for his company, the unscrupulous agent works for a verdict of suicide, although there is no sufficient occasion for adopting that explanation of the crash. Then he ventures "predictions" to bear out his verdict. "If it was suicide," he reasons, "then we are likely to find that his home life was not ideally happy. In fact I'll bet we find that his health wasn't perfect either. No doubt he has some debts as well. Those can drive a man to desperation. And we probably needn't look far to find troubles in his office too. Well, I'll look into these matters and see what I can scare up." It is evident that the hypothesis of suicide is not being tested by these predictions. Although we can call them predictions of a sort, in contrast to the hypochondriac's stream of consciousness, they are vague ones and are likely to have application in one way or another for almost any person.

The rule known as Occam's Razor, named after the medieval logician William of Occam, states that explanatory factors should not be multiplied beyond necessity. This rule cautions against making explanations more elaborate than they need to be in order to account for the phenomena in question. There are at least two kinds of violation worth noting. In the first kind one or more possibilities suggested by fancy rather than by fact appear in the hypothesis. The housewife who discovers a hole in the bread wrapper might let her thoughts drift along these lines: "Perhaps my next-door neighbor, who seems fairly prosperous, is actually starvation-poor. While I was out shopping, she may have entered my house to get a morsel of bread. To avoid suspicion she made it look like the work of a mouse." Here a mouse would be enough to explain the hole. Reference to a neighbor, an act of housebreaking, and a condition of hidden poverty would be only embroidery.

In the second type of violation the hypothesis creates a new mystery. For example, those who support someone other than Shakespeare as the author of the plays find themselves burdened by a new question: How did Shakespeare conspire to assume credit for the authorship during his own lifetime? They offer more or less ingenious answers, which vary to suit each proposed candidate, but the point is that the extra idea of mysterious conspiracy is not suggested by the facts of the case but is, instead, a by-product of the hypothesis.

The flying saucer scare of the 1950's illustrates a similar violation of Occam's rule. It began with reported sightings of unidentified flying objects. To explain these, some writers developed the hypothesis of a remote planetary civilization comparable to but more advanced than that on earth. The sightings, which included some radar trackings and puzzling photographs, were provocative enough to constitute a genuine occasion for offering hypotheses. However, to account for them by positing a whole planetful of extraordinary beings is, if not completely fanciful, at least premature in the absence of direct public evidence of such creatures. Investigators of a less romantic turn of mind have in fact succeeded in duplicating some of the reported phenomena in experiments based on a knowledge of optics and of the atmosphere.

It is neither unheard of nor unusual for highly trained inquirers to stumble into violations of the rules just cited. The boundary line between science and science fiction is not always easy to make out, particularly in the early stages of an investigation. The fact that most of us encounter scientific knowledge through such finished documents as textbooks and learned treatises does much to conceal the fact that the pursuit of knowledge involves a constant struggle to reason well.

§7   Problems in the Logic of Explanation

In the preceding chapter the practice of representing sampling by means of a formula or a simplified pattern was criticized. Similar strictures apply in the case of hypotheses. If a logician lets himself imagine that the logical pattern of explanations captures everything essential to their construction and use, he will soon find himself confronting a second application of Hume's expression of the problem of induction. Suppose that we forget the physical surroundings in which the housewife did her hypothetic reasoning and examine the following representation of her thoughts:

> I see a puzzling hole in the bread wrapper.
> If there were mice raiding our cupboards, this puzzle would be explained.
> Therefore I have some reason to believe that we have mice.

This way of describing the mouse-hypothesis already begins to remind us of a well-known fallacy in the formal calculus of propositions. If we symbolize the argument in the style of the hypothetical syllogism, the resemblance becomes more glaring:

> p is true.
> But if q were true, the truth of p would no longer be puzzling.
> Therefore we have reason to think q is true.

If now we omit all common language from our symbolization the resulting formula reads:

$$[(q \supset p) \cdot p] \supset q.$$

This is the formula for the fallacy called *affirming the consequent*. In terms of formal logic there is no necessary link between the hypothesis q and the datum or fact p. That is, p gives us no more reason than r, s, or any other sentence for asserting q. This fact makes it appear that the original mouse-hypothesis stands on just as weak a footing as does the following one:

> I see a puzzling hole in the bread wrapper.
> If there were a walrus around, and it accidentally pushed its tusk through the wrapper, this puzzling fact would be explained.
> Therefore I have some reason to believe we have a walrus.

The fact that the original hypothesis has the same form as the example just given seems to suggest that hypotheses are treacherous and arbitrary guesses. There is of course no room in a condensed formula for an account of the physical surroundings in which the mouse-hypothesis suggests itself and no room for itemizing the housewife's knowledge of the types of pest in her locality and their characteristic behavior. Reference to the conditions under which explanations are put forward would remove much of the mystery about the frequency with which men hit upon true hypotheses. If we ignore the surrounding conditions, as we necessarily and permissibly do in studying deductive reasoning, we thereby make hypotheses look like blind guesses. We also make our success in hitting upon true hypotheses appear baffling, whereas in science and daily life it is no mystery at all. Many logicians who turn to the logic of explanations with deduction-like patterns in mind see a further difficulty in characterizing the logical relation between a hypothesis and the evidence that later accumulates in its favor. No matter how many predictions confirm a hypothesis, they argue, it will never be totally confirmed or proved; no massing of evidence can advance it from a probable truth to a certainty. Now if we take this to be saying that no hypothesis is *deducible* from the evidence for it, that is true, but the statement merely reminds us of something we noted earlier, namely, that a hypothesis does not come into the world by being deduced from premisses. However, if the statement suggests that there is never a conclusive link between hypothesis and evidence, a link that would justify our regarding at least some tested hypotheses as proved beyond doubt, then it misleads us by importing a particular meaning of words like "proved" as they are used in *deductive* logic. It would be hard, for example, to see how we could further support the claim—which made its scientific appearance as a hypothesis—that the Anopheles mosquito carries malaria.

A somewhat different problem turns up in the doctrine that a hypothesis that cannot be publicly tested is no genuine hypothesis at all but a mere froth of empty words. In the second and third decades of this century a group of philosophers who called themselves The Vienna Circle made this doctrine a cornerstone of their philosophical program, Logical Positivism. Their influence on the British philosopher Alfred J. Ayer led him to popularize the new movement for the English-speaking world in his widely read *Language, Truth and Logic*.[1] The positivistic demand for testability of hypotheses as a condition for ad-

[1]Revised edition (New York: Dover Publications, Inc., 1946).

mitting them into meaningful discourse has influenced the greater part of recent discussion on scientific method.

Our early examples reveal that hypotheses quite commonly allow of being followed up with tests and that the results of such tests are important in deciding such matters as the right treatment for an injured ankle or the best means of removing a household pest. In science, as we know, it is not enough to hypothesize that a certain insect is the carrier of a dangerous disease; a hunch is only the beginning, and men have been fooled by hunches often enough to have learned they are no sure guarantors of truth. Since humans are just as capable of a wrong hypothesis as of a right one, it seems reasonable to insist that only testable hypotheses be considered, even where testing is not immediately practicable. It has become part of the economy of scientific research to favor the hypothesis that more readily lends itself to decisive testing. The first thing to notice about the demand for testability, then, is that it can function as a practical safeguard against alienating ourselves from fact. This much concerning verifiability had been said by many logicians and scientists long before Logical Positivism.

Most philosophers of science, including positivists, would agree that when we ask for an explanation of a puzzling physical fact we are asking for a reference to some efficacious physical agency capable of producing that fact. Since a physical cause ordinarily has effects beyond the one we are out to explain, we can always look for telltale signs whose presence will corroborate a hypothesis or whose absence will lead us to try a different one. A hypothesis for which no signs for or against *could* turn up for public inspection would be regarded by most philosophers as useless for purposes of natural science. To say "The Barringer Crater was dug by a troop of angels who can never be reached for questioning" would be to construct a piece of fancy outside the realm of nature studies and useless for scientific purposes.

A number of positivist philosophers have stirred up dust devils by going beyond this general agreement and assigning unlimited range to the verifiability principle. Whereas tradition reserves the term 'empirical hypothesis' for explanations occasioned by puzzling facts in the physical order, Ayer and kindred thinkers take it to mean the same as 'declarative sentence'. Any declarative sentence other than the analytic statements of mathematics and formal logic, regardless of who put it together and for what purpose, gets assimilated into the class of empirical hypotheses. This doctrine, or rather stipulation, erroneously suggests that all such sentences originate and function in the traditional and narrower sense of 'hypothesis' analyzed in this chapter. This indiscriminate new use of the term, together with the idea that testability is a necessary condition for meaningfulness, has caused alarm and confusion concerning sentences like these:

> There is a God.
> You have an immortal soul.
> We ought to help underdeveloped nations.
> Prayers are always answered.
> God created the heavens and the earth.
> Theft is wrong.

It is easy to place these sentences in their several contexts, for instance natural theology, ethics, Scripture, and so on. It is also easy to see how unlikely is the assumption that these were constructed in the manner typical of hypotheses in the ordinary sense or that they function like them, that is, by positing a physical cause to account for a puzzling fact. However, if we assume (contrary to good usage) that every declarative sentence is a hypothesis and that every genuine hypothesis should be experimentally testable, then we may be tempted to think that countless declaratives concerning matters of the deepest human importance are gravely faulty. It is helpful to remind ourselves that testability is a feature that men have adopted as a requirement for *physical explanations*. Instead of accepting testability as a condition for using this or that declarative sentence, it is of fundamental importance, then, to stop and make sure that the sentence in question is truly a hypothesis in the generally accepted sense of the term, not by virtue of a covert redefinition.

§8   Logic and Causality in Hypothetic Reasoning

A problem much discussed by recent philosophers of science concerns the nature of the mental step taken when a man reasons from a puzzling fact to its likeliest explanation. Some philosophers suggest that there must be a sort of logic, a pattern or set of rules, that guides our minds more or less directly to the correct hypothesis. A particular puzzling datum, they argue, might be explained in any number of ways. Our ability to pick out the right explanation in one or a few tries hints at the existence of a guiding logic in the background. Philosophers supporting this view see hypotheses as inferences exhibiting a logical (though not necessary) link between datum and explanation. However, they have not reached general agreement on just what the principles of that logic could be.

The opposition declares against any such logical pattern. The guiding factor in man's success with hypotheses, if one wishes to speak of guidance at all, is luck, intuition, genius, blessedness, or something equally beyond human control. Those who take this negative position see hypotheses as essentially guesses or hunches and regard it as misleading to talk as though we drew them as inferences. A hunch, they point out, is a belief for which no adequate premisses can be offered.

When we represent this problem in terms of two extremes, although by no means would most philosophers care to take one side or the other without further qualification, one can see faults on either side. The first group understands that man's success with hypotheses is no blind accident but cannot produce any general rules for obtaining true hypotheses. The second group is content to call this success inexplicable because no logical formula leading from datum to explanation can be found. The student of scientific method is thus faced with the task of threading a safe way between the two positions. To begin, we may call in question an assumption common to both points of view just described: Both sides take it as unquestioned that a particular hypothesis, for example the one that attributes Barringer Crater to a meteorite, is only one out of very many or even countless *possible* explanations. Further, it is assumed that the link between protasis and apodosis in the sentence "If a gigantic meteorite had crashed here, then just such a crater would surely have resulted" is what formal logic would call 'material implication'. Arguments involving material implication are, as formal logic teaches, substitution-arguments whose strength or weakness lies in their logical pattern; by substituting statements for variables in a certain valid pattern, one can be protected against going from true premisses to a false conclusion. In other words, one can satisfy the conditions for deductive validity. Since any self-consistent or logically possible sentence can be substituted for a variable in the calculus of propositions and since the reasoning used by the naturalist studying the crater is presumed to be fully representable in the notation of that calculus, it appears that he has a potentially infinite number of possibilities to choose from— only one of which is true. When we look at the act of propounding a hypothesis through notations supplied by deductive logic, it looks indeed like a case of finding a needle in a haystack. Considering man's success with hypotheses, it is no wonder that one side of the dispute looks for logical guidelines. And considering the slenderness of the logical link between datum and explanation, it is hardly surprising that the other side should despair of finding them.

However, when we examine the practice of formulating hypotheses, taking care not to view it through the distortion-lens of deductive logic and bearing in mind that hypotheses belong to an entirely different genus of reasonings, the problem of finding a logic of explanations begins to fade away. The person about to venture a hypothesis does not need to sift out the correct one from all logically possible sentences. The assumption that he must perform such a feat overlooks the fact that only physical possibilities concern him and that his surroundings normally afford clues as to which ones among those are likeliest. What guides the housewife to her mouse-hypothesis? Physical clues, the characteristic traces left by a common household pest. The problem of how she contrives to exclude all other logically possible explanations simply does not arise, since she is not deducing or proving anything. In a particular case she could of course err in blaming a mouse; children, we know, often tear wrappers. But that does not change the fact that mice do raid cupboards or that in her immediate circumstances, where the cupboards might be out of children's reach, a mouse is a likely suspect. "Likely," we should keep in mind, does not mean "statistically most probable" in terms of numerical odds, as has been suggested by some thinkers who try to picture all inductive reasoning in terms of statistical frequencies. Most hypotheses are propounded without consulting records of past experience.

The field of physical possibilities is harder to survey where the phenomenon in question is rare or the clues have been obscured by time. A settler gazing at the Arizona crater with no knowledge of geology or of the mechanics of impact could not be expected to come up with the meteor-hypothesis. Special knowledge and a trained eye for clues are required for that. Here as before, however, it is a knowledge of the physical possibilities, not merely the logical ones, that guides the inquirer.

A final problem concerns the concept of *cause*. In his *Treatise of Human Nature* David Hume ventured an analysis of causation from which many subsequent philosophers have found difficulty in freeing themselves. When we call one thing the cause of another, Hume said, we are relating the one to the other in three distinct respects. First, we are saying that the cause is contiguous with the effect in time and space. Second, we are saying that the cause invariably produces the effect. Third, we are asserting a necessary connection between the two such that the occurrence of the cause guarantees the occurrence of the effect. Hume argued that the last element, the necessary connection, is not given in experience but invented by the mind. Kant is another philosopher who sought to locate the necessary connection in the mind. Others, for example Alfred North Whitehead,[2] have argued that we can perceive it in ordinary experience.

Since the concept of cause is of surpassing concern in a methodological

2*Process and Reality* (New York: The Macmillan Company, 1929), p. 125.

account of causal hypotheses, it will be useful to look twice at Hume's analysis before permitting it to guide our thinking. On the first element in his definition we have little to say. In terms of familiar examples it is clear that the mouse and the wrapper it gnaws are contiguous in space and time. The same holds true for the meteorite and its crater and for the fracture and the swelling it causes. Considering the second element, we begin to find ambiguities. Massive meteorites *invariably* produce impact craters when they hit, fractures *usually* produce swelling, and mice *sometimes* gnaw through wax paper. Hume's reference to invariance in the causal relation seems to apply more strictly to the first kind of phenomena than to the second and third.

A more radical criticism can be directed toward Hume's idea of a necessary connection. The connection between the mouse and the wrapper is one of gnawing, between the meteorite and the earth one of collision, and between the fracture and the swelling one of tissue-reactions. Is the notion of a necessary connection somehow bound up with our saying that the mouse *gnaws*, the meteor *smashes into* the earth, and the injury *sets off* an increase in blood supply? Those verbs declare the kind of connection we have in mind in each of the three causal hypotheses. But where does Hume's necessary connection come in? Is it something over and above the gnawing, smashing, and setting off? If it is, then Hume is surely wrong in supposing that everyone who employs the concept of physical causation asserts a necessary connection. If it is not, then there is no mystery about the phrase "necessary connection," since it is merely a collective term for such connections as gnawing, colliding, setting off, and so on. There is of course little room for skepticism concerning whether those connections occur in the mind or in the physical world.

Some years after Hume published his *Treatise*, Kant's *Critique of Pure Reason* included as one of the postulates of all empirical thought this proposition: "Everything that happens is hypothetically necessary." In this statement of a necessary connection between cause and effect we can find a hint that the necessity in question is in the link between the *statement* of the effect and the *statement* of the cause. In other words it would be a hypothetical, linguistic, even mathematical kind of necessity, suggested perhaps by the fact that in some areas of physical science it is possible to use a formal deductive calculus to determine, for instance, the location of an unidentified mass in space that is causing irregularities in the paths of known bodies. Even so, such limited applications of necessary reasoning would not support the universal Kantian principle, as he himself realized in calling it an a priori postulate.

Although methodology must take historical notice of the influential analyses credited to Hume and Kant, it is equally important to remind ourselves that neither philosopher succeeded in representing the notion of causation as it is actually used in hypotheses. The idea of a necessary connection as they conceived it is not part of causal explanation in general.

3

Laws
and
General
Theories

§9   The Role of the Well-asked Question

In the last two chapters we emphasized particular cases, for instance, sampling a given shipment of milk for its fat content or explaining a certain crater at a specified place on the map. The results in any one case of sampling or explaining might accidentally hold for other cases as well, but caution requires that each new problem be separately investigated in relation to its surroundings. In the sciences, however, we also encounter knowledge of a wider sort, such as empirical formulas, laws that hold for all or most facts of a particular type, and comprehensive theories that bring dissimilar kinds of fact into unity. These we must now consider.

In daily experience we learn of many physical regularities. The stars wheel about a point in the heavens; the planets maintain their schedules; the moon goes through its phases in sight of the earth; mammals die without air; larvae and molds form on decaying food. Our knowledge of such facts is as solidly based as anything science can tell us. Common knowledge, however, is not science but a kind of ore from which science can be mined. Our examples reflect the dependable repetitions of nature and are expressed in common language. We live and die in the presence of these repetitions, and the routine of human life is sufficient to etch them on even the most sluggish and uninquisitive minds. Science, however, transforms raw data into systematic knowledge gathered under clearly delimited subject matters with standardized vocabularies. In a science, astronomy for instance, the content of passive observation is screened through a series of deliberate questions put to nature. This process begins when the inquirer seeks to find out something further about a regularity such as those we listed and raises a question:

Is it the stars' own motion that takes them once around the earth each day?

How can we represent on paper the path of Mars?

What keeps the moon at about the same distance from the earth?

What component of air do mammals require?

Do maggots form spontaneously on rotting meat?

The practice of posing such questions and tracking down answers makes the difference between man as a mere recorder of regularities, a remembering animal, and man as an active partner with nature in the production of settled knowledge. This is not to suggest, as some philosophers would have it, that the mind imposes order upon nature and creates rather than discovers her laws. It is merely a reminder that the knowledge of nature's workings does not come to those who passively wait for it. Science is an activity, and like most human pursuits it is a stumbling one. The history of science reveals how closely progress and retardation have been bound up with the art of posing questions.

The person constructing the well-asked question first of all seeks to distinguish between what he knows and what he is inclined to take for granted. To cite a famous example, the quest for a clear picture of planetary motion was hampered for centuries by two beliefs that intruded themselves into the wording of the astronomer's question: "How can the path of Mars *around the earth* be diagrammed *in strictly circular figures?*" The most strenuous efforts of imagination were needed before sixteenth- and seventeenth-century astronomy could free itself from treating as indisputable the belief that the earth must be central to all celestial motions and that those motions must be uniformly circular. These beliefs were all the more tenacious for being reasoned; behind them stood classical pieties concerning the changeless and divine order of the heavens.

Keeping a clear distinction between what we assume, even where there seem to be excellent reasons for assuming it, and what we know, can be as difficult in terrestrial sciences as in those dealing with the reaches of space. Before the microscope came into use naturalists claimed evidence of spontaneous generation in the fact that a bucket of humus or topsoil that had been sifted and placed in a sunny spot would presently give rise to grass, weeds, toadstools, and even insects. Once the microscope had revealed seeds, eggs, and spores tiny enough to pass through a sieve, the evidence-value of these observations dropped to zero. When biologists ceased to hold as final the old assumption that the limit of biological minuteness coincides with the limit of naked-eye visibility, they could see how even genius had spent years of wasted effort.

Freeing ourselves from questionable assumptions is only a negative condition for putting a well-asked question to nature. Before the experimental attitude can be productive, two further conditions must be met. First, related general knowledge must come abreast of the problem at issue. For example, when the spontaneous generation of maggots was an accepted doctrine, naturalists saw adequate observational evidence for it in the fact that larvae appear on spoiled meat with no manifest cause. Taken in abstraction from any knowledge of the breeding habits of flies, these observations in the long run had no value. General knowledge had not reached a level at which investigators could discern just where they had to exercise control over the surroundings (in this instance by screening the meat from insects) in order to get a decisive result.

The second and related condition is that physical techniques must come up to a level of sophistication parallel with the growth of general knowledge. Long after the microscope was invented an important faction of naturalists continued to hold a modified form of the doctrine of spontaneous generation for microbes and intestinal worms. Water kept in a sealed flask, they reasoned, soon teems with bacteria, yeasts, and protozoa. Louis Pasteur (1822–1895), whose experiments with fermentation and sterilization had pushed his own unpublished knowledge beyond that of his contemporaries, found himself in a position to settle the problem. He exposed flasks of boiled water to the air, some at sea level and others at high mountain altitudes, and he noted that organisms appeared only in the former. In another experiment he showed that beef broth, if boiled and immediately sealed against air, can be stored indefinitely without producing organisms. Break the seal enough to let a little air enter, he demonstrated, and within hours the broth swarms with living creatures. Here the physical techniques required for producing sterile media were essential to solving the problem. Boiling is a simple means for effecting sterilization, but the problem at hand required also that the condition of sterility be sustained long enough to guarantee an unambiguous result. This in turn called for new techniques to protect the sterile medium from the intrusion of air, an invisible carrier of spores.

To sum up, the movement from a uniformity found in everyday experience to a scientific generalization begins with a well-asked question. That question may take up little space in a scientific treatise yet may require a great stretch of historical time, for its formulation often involves the slow, painful separation of what men know from what it never occurs to them to doubt. Nor is the well-asked question itself of any use unless the asker commands techniques and instruments to aid him in putting his question to nature.

§10   Putting the Question to Nature

The sixteenth century marked a transition from passive to active efforts in fathoming the workings of the physical world. Basic to the new approach was the idea that man can take steps that will *force* nature to reveal her underlying laws. Forcing her to divulge a general law is analogous to the familiar practice of forcing a stratified class of objects to yield a representative sample of itself. As Pasteur's experiments showed, control over the immediate surroundings makes the difference between a loosely conceived inspection of nature and a conclusive study, just as between an indeterminate fraction of a population and a telling sample. There is on the whole nothing mysterious in the idea of extorting the truth from nature. The contrast between a passive observation and an experiment that forces nature to answer takes us back to the principle mentioned in Chapter 1 when we were drawing a boundary between deductive and experimental methods. To get at the truth the experimenter takes pains to exclude or at least make allowances for any physical possibilities that might affect the accuracy of his result. The experimental sciences owe much of the delay in their maturation to the fact that even after the experimental attitude had taken hold decades were needed before men could become fully aware of the relevant physical possibilities and could develop techniques for controlling them.

Galileo's work illustrates an early advance in the controlled interrogation of nature. Until the beginning of the seventeenth century it was said that heavier bodies fall faster than light ones. It seemed only natural; feathers and playing cards clearly took longer to reach the ground than a lead plummet dropped from the same height. The law stating that gravitational force is proportional to the mass of a body, a law allowing that air or another surrounding medium can slow up a falling object, had not yet been enunciated. Today in a routine demonstration in high school physics the instructor drops a feather and a steel ball side by side in an evacuated glass tube and points out that they hit bottom simultaneously. In Galileo's day the common knowledge that some bodies fall more slowly than others was never in question. However, a new kind of concern had attached itself to the phenomenon of motion, and a new kind of question began to appear: Are there underlying regularities or laws of motion masked by accidental circumstances such as intervening media? Common knowledge was too unrefined to settle this question. The new form of question asked whether *freely* falling bodies all descend at the same rate. To decide that, it was necessary to manufacture a set of conditions that nature herself does not provide the inquirer, conditions that permit him to discount the medium through which terrestrial objects ordinarily fall. In Galileo's experiments a new kind of science was born, promising vastly greater predictive power than the Aristotelian analysis of motion but attended by its own Democritean temptation to oversimplify the nature of physical reality.

The use of deliberate experiments in the search for laws of nature is not always possible. When we are dealing with subjects hard to approach, such as earthquakes or wild animals, or when we must wait for the changing seasons to bring our data into view, as in astronomy, careful observations must suffice. This limitation can make it doubly difficult to determine a clear answer, as the history of astronomy illustrates. In the Ptolemaic or earth-centered picture of the universe (developed by the Alexandrian astronomer Ptolemy in the years A.D. 127–151) the orbit of Mars was represented as a circle on which were hung numerous smaller loops, called epicycles, to stand for observed retrograde movements of the planet. This picture agreed with spotty observations of the path of Mars and with the belief in perfect circularity as the only suitable form for celestial motion. The wooliness of the Ptolemaic picture offended some sixteenth-century astronomers; it seemed a makeshift, ill-matching the grand simplicity of the night skies. Nicholas Copernicus (1473–1543), still clinging to the circularist assumption but putting the geocentric one in brackets, tried to simplify the Ptolemaic diagram in one respect by placing the sun at the center and regarding the earth as one of its planets. This shift gave him some play in the number of epicycles needed, but in principle it remained the same sort of ragged picture, because astronomers could add more loops to make it agree with later observations, as had happened with Ptolemy.

The observations that called in question the old assumption of circularity were supplied by Tycho Brahe (1546–1601), whose improved instruments enabled him to track a planet continuously across the sky instead of plotting its path at nightly intervals. Johannes Kepler (1571–1630) inherited Tycho's records. Allowing that they impugned the belief in circular motion, he set about finding a type of oval that would match the observed path of Mars yet would not oblige him to add loops. The curve of an ellipse agreed exactly. In 1609 he announced two laws:

1. The planet traces an ellipse with the sun at one focus.
2. A straight line between sun and planet sweeps out equal areas in equal times.

Kepler thus achieved a breakthrough in the application of exact mathematical reckoning to physical phenomena. To the student of scientific methods his work is illuminating not so much in the laws themselves, which belong properly to celestial mechanics, as in the stage setting for their discovery. Few case studies in the history of science offer as clear a basis for distinguishing the passive and active elements involved in putting a decisive question to nature. Tycho's active role as the improver of instruments balances his more passive role as the skillful observer recording what he sees without letting his own circularist views color the results. Kepler, on the passive side, leaned upon Tycho's observations and upon new techniques in clock-making that made it possible for time to figure in his laws. On the active side it was Kepler's part to shake off the circularist preconception. Only after all these conditions had been fulfilled was he in a position to discern the laws of planetary motion.

The standing of Kepler's first law was reinforced when Isaac Newton (1642–1727) showed that an ellipse is the only path possible for a planet held in tow by the sun's gravitation. This unforeseen corroboration suggests an instructive contrast between Kepler's law and empirical formulas of a more *ad hoc* sort. Bode's Law (named for John Bode of Berlin who worked on it *circa* 1772), was an attempt to make arithmetical the relative distances between sun and planets. He took a series of 4's, letting the first 4 stand for the distance between the sun and Mercury, the innermost planet. To the second 4 he added 3, to the third he added 6, and so on, doubling the number added each time, until he had the series: 4, 7, 10, 16, 28, 52, 100. The series up to 100 gives a fair approximation of relative distances between the sun and Mercury, Venus, Earth, Mars, the asteroid belt between Mars and Jupiter, then Jupiter itself, and finally Saturn. The next number in the series is 196, which happens to correspond to the distance of the then undiscovered planet Uranus. The following number is 388, which ought to correspond to Neptune. However, Neptune is in fact at about 300 on Bode's scale.

In its first heyday Bode's formula stood as a curiosity. It still provokes flurries of interest in connection with fresh speculations about the origin of the solar system. His choice of the number 4, however, had the look of something not suggested by the facts but contrived in order to fit them. It carried little intuitive promise of being borne out when the next test case came along or of being itself subsumed under a more general law. Kepler's search for the true path of Mars, although it might at first appear to be in the same pattern as Bode's search for a regular numerical progression, was prompted by the planet's known schedules, which suggested a determinate orbit. In contrast, no facts suggested a regular relation of distances between sun and planets, although a dim hint of such a relation might be gathered from the nebular hypothesis in eighteenth-century astronomy. Physical laws are discovered by making a transition from observed regularities via well-asked questions, but where no strong regularity presents itself the usual occasion for enunciating a general law is missing. Even if Bode's formula had been found to hold for Neptune and Pluto, one could ask whether it should rank as a law rather than as a striking fact (on a par, for instance, with the fact that the orbits of Mercury and Pluto, the innermost and outermost planets, have the most compressed ellipses).

§11   Theories

The word 'theory' is sometimes used to stand for any untested idea, as "the theory that life exists on other planets," and sometimes for a studied explanation of a particular fact, as "the theory that Indians originally migrated to North America from Asia." The former meaning suggests freewheeling speculation, the latter what we have been calling hypothesis. 'Theory' comes from a Greek word meaning a *beholding* or *seeing*. There is an analogy between the way in which a hypothesis (as in the crater example) closes up a gap of puzzlement and the way in which an explanation of a wider sort (for instance, the theory of evolution) enables men to set their minds at ease about a broad range of diverse facts assembled by geologists, paleontologists, embryologists, and other natural scientists. After Darwin naturalists found it possible to 'behold' fossil remains of extinct monsters without feeling that they were confronting a streak of inexplicability in nature. The kind of beholding or vision offered by a mature theory is primarily mental rather than visual; in this sense a theory is an idea or manageable handful of ideas by reference to which men can throw light on a large class of physical facts. Although it is risky to insist on the distinction for all cases, a law, in contrast to a theory, does not explain anything but expresses the regular mode of action to be expected from a certain class of phenomena or the regular mode of action of a force.

In studying the conception, structure, and uses of scientific theories it is important to make ourselves aware of their diversity. By pointing up key differences between theories in, say, physics and biology we can safeguard ourselves against the too common tendency to select a particular kind of theory and hold it up as the ideal.

The most striking if not the most characteristic example of theory-construction on a grand scale must be credited to Isaac Newton. Aware of Kepler's discoveries in celestial mechanics and of Galileo's experiments with falling bodies (which had led the Italian to posit the idea of a gravitational force), Newton asked whether a single universal force might not govern the march of planets round the sun, the movements of the moon and other planetary satellites, and the fall of a dropped pebble on earth. If whatever force makes a pebble fall at sea level does the same to a lump of coal at the bottom of a mine and a piece of ice on a mountain peak, might it not be working as far out as the moon? In keeping with Galileo's axiom that bodies in motion tend to proceed in a straight line unless acted upon by outside forces, can we not think of the moon's motion as basically a straight-line motion compounded by a falling-toward-earth motion? Assuming this compound motion can be shown, the next step would be to construe the orbits of planets in the same way with the sun at the gravitational center. Aided by the differential calculus that he helped invent, Newton calculated what the moon's path would be if its motion were of the kind he suspected. When he found that his calculations agreed with the facts, Newton proceeded to formulate a set of principles embodied in all gross inanimate motions, headed by the celebrated Inverse Square Law: "Every particle in the universe is attracted to every other with a force directly proportional as the product of the masses and inversely as the square of the distance."

Although Newton himself denied that he was propounding 'hypotheses' in these investigations, for he wished to disassociate his work from that of nonempirical thinkers who speculated about occult forces, it is not hard to discern a kind of explanatory element in the notion of a universal force and more particularly in the idea that the motions of moon and planets are compound. The Newtonian system proved general and flexible enough to cover not only the regular motions of planets, comets, and pendulums, but a number of erratic motions as well, though some of the latter were not adequately treated until the time of Einstein. The most dramatic confirmation of Newton's work occurred in the discovery of a new planet, Neptune. The planet Uranus, discovered in 1781, showed deviations from a true ellipse. Working on the hypothesis that a more remote planet troubled the course of Uranus by its gravitational presence, the English astronomer John Couch Adams and the Frenchman Urbain LeVerrier independently calculated the probable location of the disturbing mass. In 1846 LeVerrier wrote to an official at the Berlin Observatory: "Direct your telescope to a point on the ecliptic in the constellation Aquarius, in longitude 326°, and you will find within a degree of that point a new planet appearing like a star of 9th magnitude and having a perceptible disk." The official, John Galle, found the new planet less than two moon-diameters from the point named by LeVerrier.

Newton's synthesis of Galileo's terrestrial laws and Kepler's celestial laws amalgamated two domains that men had always regarded as radically dissimilar. Between the earthy and perishable things around them and the seemingly changeless luminaries above, men knew of no ties except the loose one of spatial relationship and the even weaker ones claimed by astrologers. Galileo's telescope, trained on the moon, sun, and planets, had revealed evidence that shattered the two-story view of the universe. Now, thanks to Newton and those on whose work he had built, men could speak in a single breath of every particle in the universe and express in mathematical terms the laws governing all inanimate motions. Moreover, if a particular body appeared at first to defy those laws, calculations based upon them could be expected to reveal other forces causing the deviations. Understandably, therefore, Newton's achievement seized the Western imagination and led many to think of physics as the paragon of all empirical sciences, corresponding to Euclid's geometry in the mathematical realm. Many an earnest psychologist or sociologist apologizes for the fact that his science is not, or is not yet, a science in the Newtonian sense, that is, a small set of formulas and principles from which individual behavior can be predicted in much the same way that astronomers predict an eclipse. But are apologies called for? In Newton, as in Einstein later, the fullness of time brought together a genius for theorizing and a domain in which certain kinds of cyclical and otherwise repeatable events lend themselves to mathematical treatment. However, not every scientific subject exhibits that initial kind of order. Too one-sided a preoccupation with physics can lead one to exaggerate the interest of theorists in predicting and to underplay their interest in explaining. A great deal of scientific theory-construction in biology, paleontology, and geology, to name only a few areas, is valued apart from any prospect of forcing it into calculus-like patterns.

At this point it will be helpful to consider a theory in biology and to notice some applications of it that are primarily explanatory and only incidentally predictive.

Charles Darwin (1809–1892) made himself familiar with a number of different kinds of facts in biology and geology, each kind represented by numerous instances. First, a gradually accumulating fossil record showed the remains of animal and plant species that have no living representatives on earth. Second, forms of life on islands tended to differ more or less from their counterparts on the mainland, depending upon the length of time since the islands had become separated. Third, animals of many species possessed nonfunctioning organs. Certain whales, for example, had teeth that never erupted through the gums. Fourth, changes in livestock and plant life as a result of artificial selection and crossbreeding had been known about for centuries. Fifth, embryologists had pointed out likenesses, some of them startling, between lower forms of life and various stages of development in mammalian embryos. Over the years knowledge of facts like these had accumulated to such an extent that the need to make them intelligible was felt by naturalists in every part of the world. It seemed impossible to account for these facts if one supposed that living species had always worn the same appearance they presented to modern man.

To Darwin and a few contemporaries this mass of indigestible data suggested an idea destined to alter the course of Western thought. Darwin's theory, as presented in *The Origin of Species* (1859), is built around three primary propositions:

1. More creatures of any species are born, hatch, or germinate than the food supply can support; hence individuals of a species find themselves in a struggle for existence. (Man is a special case under this generalization, since he can exercise some prescient control over his food supply.)
2. Chance variations sometimes occur in individuals, making them slightly different from their parents, and these new traits can in some instances be passed on to offspring. (The budding sciences of genetics and cell theory would presently increase knowledge of the actual mechanics of variation.)
3. When a new trait gives the individual an edge in the struggle for existence, the individual's chances for reproduction are enhanced by that much and the new trait will tend to spread through succeeding generations.

The application of this theory to particular puzzles is significantly different from the application of theories cast in mathematical notations. We may notice first the strong likeness between Darwin's main idea, the gradual development of species, and a typical hypothesis such as our example about the meteorite and the crater. Each is put forward as an explanation in order to set minds at rest about a puzzling configuration of facts. The explanations, moreover, are sought quite apart from any prospect of using them to predict the future. General predictions of what we may expect to find if the explanations are true (for example, fragments of meteorite in the crater or occasional instances of mutant individuals), are of course useful for helping to confirm them, but the value of the explanation does not depend on any usefulness in predicting the *next* meteorite or mutation. There are sciences that help us to predict the next eclipse or planetary conjunction, and we value them highly; still, the desire to know what will happen next is only one of the appetites that lead men to propose hypotheses and theories.

Looking beyond the similarity between the Darwinian theory and the narrower hypothesis, we can discern an equally marked difference. Darwin's propositions do not directly explain any of the facts that prompted him to formulate them, whereas the reference to a meteorite does directly explain the crater. The wider theory is much too general to do that. Instead, a connection between the theory and a particular fact is made by *talking through* to the fact in a manner suggested and permitted by the theory. This talking (or writing) is not to be confused with any form of calculating, as an example from Darwin's book will make clear:

> The Greenland whale is one of the most wonderful animals in the world, and the baleen, or whale-bone, one of its greatest peculiarities. The baleen consists of a row, on each side, of the upper jaw, of about three hundred plates or laminae, which stand close together transversely to the longer axis of the mouth. Within the main row there are some subsidiary rows. The extremities and inner margins of all the plates are frayed into stiff bristles, which clothe the whole gigantic palate, and serve to strain or sift the water, and thus to secure the minute prey on which these great animals subsist. The middle or longest lamina in the Greenland whale is ten, twelve, or even fifteen feet in length; the middle lamina being in one species, according to Scoresby, four feet, in another three, in another eighteen inches, and in the *Balaenoptera rostrata* only about nine inches in length. The quality of the whale-bone also differs in the different species.
>
> With respect to the baleen, Mr. Mivart remarks that if it "had once attained such a size and development as to be at all useful, then its preservation and augmentation within serviceable limits would be promised by natural selection alone. But how to obtain the beginning of such development?" In the answer, it may be asked, why should not the early progenitors of the whales with baleen have possessed a mouth constructed something like the lamellated beak of a duck? Ducks, like whales, subsist by sifting the mud and water; and the family has sometimes been called *Criblatores*, or sifters. I hope that I may not be misconstrued into saying that the progenitors of whales did actually possess mouths lamellated like the beak of a duck. I wish only to show that this is not incredible, and that the immense plates of baleen in the Greenland whale might have been developed from such lamellae by finely graduated steps, each of service to its possssor.[1]

In this passage Darwin takes up the question of how whales might have begun to acquire their sprays of baleen. He cannot *deduce* an answer from the general idea of natural selection, but neither is he left helpless. The theory offers what might be called a form or matrix for particular explanations. The investigator who perceives a particular puzzle, for instance, how baleen began to develop, must then use *discursive* language (augmented by technical terminology), in order to fill in that form. He must find a new way from the theory to the fact, bringing in relevant information from paleontology, geography, genetics, and the biology of the species in question. The plausibility of the result need not be weighed in terms of predictions to be compared with later experience, although subsequent knowledge could conceivably lead biologists to certify or reject or amend it. It is grounded, though fallibly, in a general understanding of the ways of nature.

[1] *The Origin of Species*, Chap. VII.

Darwin's statement that it is "not incredible" that whales "might" have had duckbilled ancestors sounds modest compared with LeVerrier's triumphant prediction of Neptune's position. Given Newton's formulas, data on the orbit of Uranus, and the appropriate mathematical techniques, LeVerrier was able to calculate on paper where the suspected mass should be found. But in a science dealing with the world of living species, which little resembles a system of inanimate masses in regular motion, human needs may demand of a theory merely that it open lines of discourse. It is neither necessary nor useful, in other words, that every science worthy of the name be set up as a system in which a few supremely general laws can be linked to observed facts by tight calculations. Nor does science as a whole need to aspire to such a model as its finished form.

The need for discursive explanations in the life sciences and in social studies by no means excludes mathematics from those domains. On the contrary, mathematics is indispensible for measurement, statistics, and countless other purposes. Nor are predictions excluded. At one time Darwin predicted that the population of foxes on an island he visited would soon become extinct owing to their puppy-like tameness. A few years later they had all been slaughtered for their pelts. The prediction, however, was not deduced from Darwin's theory or reached by calculations in the manner of LeVerrier. Like a prognosis in medicine, it was enunciated on the basis of an appraisal of the immediate circumstances, with half a lifetime's schooling in the background. The absence of any deductive connection between theory and prediction is clear from the fact that the foxes might have continued to flourish for one reason or another (protection from the Crown, for instance, or the remoteness of their habitat), without upsetting Darwin's theory. In contrast, failure to find an actual mass along the lines of force indicated by the waverings of Uranus would have prompted a serious re-examination of Newton's principles.

To sum up, scientific theories of the wider sort exhibit irreducible differences in mode of origin, application to particular cases, over-all structure, conformability to an axiomatic model, and types of reasoning employed. It is in fact somewhat misleading to speak of the gist of such a theory or to cull out a few summary sentences from Darwin and call those the essence of his theory, in abstraction from all the illustrations, cautions, and subsidiary reasonings packed around those ideas in *The Origin of Species* and in later evolutionary literature. The same holds for treating the theory of Newtonian mechanics apart from the family of descriptive and mathematical techniques bound up with its uses. Theory-construction proceeds in a variety of valid, useful, and important ways, depending upon the kinds of facts under study and the kinds of questions men want answered. In the light of these distinctions it would seem that the dream of axiomatizing biology, psychology, and their sister sciences has been entertained without full awareness of the variety of problems the sciences consider. To speak of deducing or calculating what happened long ago or will happen next in a sea, a jungle, a scattered species, or a human society caters more to man's craving for mathematical elegance than to his hunger for knowledge. The very mildest caution one could venture here is that a failure to notice significantly different types of theory can lead to a one-sided view of a many-sided subject.

The supreme value of theory, then, lies in the power it confers upon human beings to explain the phenomena of nature. Darwin's theory supplied a speculative background tolerant of questions such as "How might the whale have developed as a species so as to be able to feed on plankton?" The theory presents a general vision of nature's ways and means, and by reference to this vision the inquirer can enlarge the domain of the intelligible. The ability to predict future events, on the other hand, enlarges the domain of the certain.

§12　Theorizing and Models

The concepts of genetic variation, millennia of geological time, and survival through advantageous traits enable men to take in stride the fossils and other phenomena that were baffling prior to Darwin's age. Besides conferring that psychological blessing, these concepts also help provide a kind of framed picture of the history of living forms. They make possible a summary of past changes in terms of elements and forces still with us and more or less familiar to us. In this respect Darwin's picture of the past captures a sensuous array which the individual man's organs of perception cannot possibly range over, much as a speeded-up film reveals in half a minute the germination of a bean during several days.

The broad field of vision opened up by a theory is by no means a substitute for detailed hypotheses that explain particular facts. It satisfies a quite different appetite that might be regarded as more immediate and sensuous than intellectual: It enables men to construct and reason about models and analogues embodying the essential ideas of the theory. One kind of model is the symbolic, in which algebraic or verbal signs are manipulated in consonance with the theory. Thus Newton in his moon experiment isolated on paper the earth-moon complex from the sun and other planets, counting the rest of the cosmos as the fine dust of the balance. In a similar way an economist wishing to simplify the world's monetary tangles for his students might first ask them to imagine a primitive island society in which banana plants are the only form of exchangeable property. Next he might introduce coconuts and cowrie shells to facilitate trade with neighboring islands. Later he might bring in a coinage system, a treasury, and related institutions.

Less discursive and more directly sensuous than the economist's model would be a cartoon movie picturing the motions in the solar system or the development of mammalian species from one-celled beginnings. Abstract laws of probability-theory have been effectively illustrated by a machine that dumps a cup of beads over a row of vertical tubes; the beads bounce into the open tubes and exhibit a 'normal' curve, with the middle tubes catching the most beads and the extremes the fewest. An optimally sensuous model might be instanced by a curved conical well in which a rolling steel ball describes the orbital swings of a satellite caught in the earth's gravitational field. In this example the artificer supplies a visible and tangible counterpart to the unseen attraction between earth and its satellite.

Worlds and societies carved in miniature can serve a variety of scientific purposes. Their most general function is to supplement theories by making them more perspicuous through reference to the sensible and familiar. Models enable men to feel more at ease with such unobservables as gravitational force and atoms, abstract principles of probability and the like, and humanly unsurveyable magnitudes such as the solar system and geological epochs.

4

Other
Emphases
in
Methodology

§13 The Syllogistic Paradigm of Science

Each of the preceding chapters concerns itself with a broad division of
empirical reasonings and emphasizes the differences between one type
and another in order to notice the special safeguards built into each.
This chapter examines some classic methodological approaches that
highlight quite different aspects of scientific practice.

One such position, first defined in Aristotle's *Posterior Analytics*, con-
siders syllogism the primary instrument of scientific reasoning and
syllogistic demonstration the goal of science. In contrast with Renaissance
and modern science, the aim of Aristotle's science is not discovery but
what he calls 'the reasoned fact'. Following Aristotle's specifications we
can put together two premises, for example, "All horned animals possess a third stomach" and "Deer are horned animals," and from these
infer "Therefore deer possess a third stomach." This syllogism brings out
a relationship between an anatomical fact about deer and a wider generalization based on an observed common property (a third stomach)
that belongs uniquely to horned animals.

Aristotle regarded the relationship between these facts as a causal
one and the inference itself as a type of causal explanation. The next
example will help us to see what he meant:

> ... we can also demonstrate that the vine has broad leaves because it is
> deciduous. Thus, let D be broad-leaved, E deciduous, F vine. Then E inheres
> in F (since every vine is deciduous), and D in E (for every deciduous
> plant has broad leaves) : therefore every vine has broad leaves, and the
> cause is its deciduous character.[1]

[1]*Posterior Analytics*, 98 b 10–16. Trans. W. D. Ross.

Here the fact that vines have broad leaves stands with another fact, namely, that vines are deciduous. The conclusion "Vines have broad leaves" does not emerge as a bit of new knowledge like a theorem of geometry; it was known to begin with. Instead it now 'stands to reason', as we say, once we understand that the property 'broad-leaved' has exactly the same range of instantiation in the plant kingdom as the property 'deciduous'. A similarly valid inference can be made by simply converting the major premiss to read "All broad-leaved plants are deciduous," putting the first conclusion in as a minor and inferring "All vines are deciduous." The causal link or element of reason in 'the reasoned fact', as Aristotle understood it, consists in the unfailing coincidence of two distinct properties within a definable range of beings such that the presence of either property is a sure sign of the other.

The preoccupation with discovery in Renaissance and later science led away from Aristotle's syllogistic method. However, his methodological writings also hint at a method of demonstration that would increase knowledge if it were workable. Aristotle thought that if men could grasp the *essential definition* of 'horse', 'elephant', 'oak tree', and so on, they could hope to demonstrate certain properties belonging uniquely and universally to horses, elephants, or other natural beings, much in the way that geometers prove properties of triangles and other figures. Aristotle supplies no clear and finished examples, and through the centuries this design for science, though much puzzled about, has remained unrealized. The essential definitions, which would identify both the genus and the specific difference that distinguishes, say, horses from all kindred species, are hard to come by. Our lack of such definitions should not, however, be taken to mean that men are constitutionally and forever unable to find out the meanings of words like 'horse'. It would be very odd if this were so, since we experience no trouble in picking out horses from related species in a menagerie. A better way of expressing it might be to say that knowing the meanings of such words is not equivalent to having an essential definition. For purposes of geometry, on the other hand, essential definitions (either given directly as definitions or implied by rules for constructing this or that figure) are intimately bound up with what comes afterward in the science. In this aspect of his scientific program Aristotle took his inspiration from geometry but was unable to carry it through to new 'theorems'.

Although Aristotle first enunciated the syllogistic paradigm of science, his own researches were in no way bound by its limitations. His name is associated with much groundbreaking work of an empirical kind, particularly in the life sciences.

§14   The Baconian Paradigm of Science

Francis Bacon (1561–1626) was distressed by the type of syllogistic science just discussed, which some of his contemporaries practiced at the expense of systematic observation and experiment. On the other side, he objected to the kind of experimentalism that kept proper vigil over nature but disdained what he called "philosophy," that is, general explanatory principles. In his *New Organon*, published in England in 1620 and so named with a reference to the *Organon* or logical treatises of Aristotle, Bacon sought to design a method that would keep a balance between the empirical content of science and its rational or explanatory content.

Bacon's design requires that the scientific observer set up three lists or tables. The first he calls the Table of Essence and Presence, which brings together all known instances of a particular property whose nature is under investigation. To inquire into the nature of heat, for example, Bacon illustrates with a table of twenty-seven instances, leaving room at the end for more. The table begins:

1.   The rays of the sun, especially in summer and at noon.
2.   The rays of the sun reflected and condensed, as . . . in burning-glasses and mirrors.
3.   Fiery meteors.
4.   Burning thunderbolts.
5.   Eruptions of flame from the cavities of mountains.
6.   All flame.[2]

The second table, called the Table of Deviation, or of Absence in Proximity, takes note of instances in which heat is absent, correlating these as nearly as possible with items in the first table. Thus he begins:

1.   The rays of the moon and of stars and comets. . . .
2.   The rays of the sun in what is called the middle regions of the air (at high altitudes) . . . .
3.   The reflection of the rays of the sun in regions near the polar circles. . . .
4.   (The sun's rays through a concave lens.)
5.   (The moon's rays through a burning-glass.)
6.   (The heat of a hot iron or stone through a burning-glass.) [3]

A third table must take account of instances in which the property is found in differing degrees. This Table of Degrees will record the

[2]*New Organon*, II, xi.
[3]*Ibid.*, II, xii.

increase and decrease of the quality in one subject as well as its amount in different subjects. Bacon's illustrative list begins with this comparison:

1. In solid and tangible bodies we find nothing which is in its nature originally hot. For no stone, metal, sulphur, fossil, wood, water, or carcass of animal is found to be hot. And the hot water in baths seems to be heated by external causes; whether it be by flame or subterraneous fire, such as is thrown up from Aetna and many other mountains, or by the conflict of bodies, as heat is caused in the dissolutions of iron and tin. There is therefore no degree of heat palpable to the touch in animate substances; but they differ in degree of cold, wood not being equally cold with metal. . . .[4]

With the three tables filled in, Bacon suggests, the proper work of induction may begin. The mind, in other words, can attend to the broad and firm empirical base established by observation and bring its rational powers to bear in grasping the true nature of heat. For example, since the sun's rays are hot, we may reason that heat is not solely an earth-element. Again, since fire is a familiar earthly and subterranean phenomenon, the nature of heat is not uniquely celestial. Proceeding in this manner, Bacon develops a list of fourteen rejected explanations of the nature of heat. This part of the method clears the way for "true Induction," which must culminate in an affirmative solution. The mind is now ready to extract the "First Vintage" of its efforts. To begin, a review of the tables shows heat to be a species of the genus motion. Next, Bacon lists four "specific differences" that serve to define the particular type of motion he identifies with heat:

The first difference then is this. Heat is an expansive motion, whereby a body strives to dilate and stretch itself to a larger sphere or dimension than it had previously occupied. This difference is most observable in flame, where the smoke or thick vapor manifestly dilates and expands itself into flame. . . .

The second difference is a modification of the former; namely, that heat is a motion expansive or toward the circumference but with this condition, that the body has at the same time a motion upwards. . . .

The third specific difference is this; that heat is a motion of expansion, not uniformly of the whole body together, but in the smaller parts of it; and at the same time checked, repelled, and beaten back, so that the body acquires a motion alternative, perpetually quivering, striving and struggling, and irritated by repercussion, whence springs the fury of fire and heat. . . .

The fourth specific difference is a modification of the last; it is, that the preceding motion of stimulation or penetration must be somewhat rapid and not sluggish, and must proceed by particles, minute indeed, yet not the finest of all, but a degree larger. . . .[5]

4*Ibid.*, II, xiii.
5*Ibid.*, II, xx.

With these differences settled, Bacon concludes:

> Now from this our First Vintage it follows that the Form or true definition of heat (heat, that is, in relation to the universe, not simply in relation to man) is in few words as follows: *Heat is a motion, expansive, restrained, and acting in its strife upon the smaller particles of bodies.* But the expansion is thus modified: *while it expands all ways, it has at the same time an inclination upwards.* And the struggle in the particles is modified also: *it is not sluggish, but hurried and with violence.*[6]

Expressing this idea in terms suggestive of experimental verification, Bacon writes:

> If in any natural body you can excite a dilating or expanding motion, and can so repress this motion and turn it back upon itself, that the dilation shall not proceed equably, but have its way in one part and be counteracted in another, you will undoubtedly generate heat.[7]

If men of science have not adopted Bacon's paradigm of scientific method, it is not because the paradigm itself contains anything fundamentally alien to the spirit of science. Elements of all the methods we have discussed are present in Bacon's account. Taken as a grand formula for the conduct of scientific inquiry, however, it has defects apart from any errors of fact that may be contained in Bacon's example. First, the range and variety of scientific concern extend far beyond Bacon's interest in finding definitions or pondering the nature of this or that quality. Second, except in very special circumstances the construction of massive tables of instances is uneconomical; in most scientific inquiries such lists are simply not needed. Atomic theory, for example, provides an explanation of heat in terms of the agitation of particles, without resting upon an enumeration of instances. Third, the mind's transition from an array of data, for instance concerning heat phenomena, to the judgment that heat is a form of motion is essentially a categorical or conceptual transition; that is, it brings the concept of heat under the more inclusive concept of motion. The inquiry, then, to the extent that it is successful, can culminate only in a definition: Heat is a form of motion having the specific characteristics A, B, C, and D.

Without challenging the fact that definitions have their place in natural science, we may note that subsuming the concept *heat* under a wider one is not the same as bringing certain phenomena under laws of nature. The difference does not constitute a fault in Bacon's intent but rather illustrates a shift of scientific interest away from prose equivalences, that is, definitions expressing genus and specific difference, toward equations and other quantitative formulas that can be filled in with

[6]*Loc. cit.*
[7]*Loc. cit.*

numbers. These would make possible not only prediction and, ultimately, control of phenomena such as heat, but also the understanding or "philosophy" that Bacon prized. This understanding was to develop in terms of laws and theories rather than of essences or definitions. Particular phenomena such as heat transfer and conductivity would presently be describable by means of mathematical formulas; a wider kinetic theory would take account of energy transformations involving heat, light, and mechanical force.

As regards the exploitation of nature's laws and powers, the quantitative or functional approach in science is superior to the Baconian pursuit of essences. The basis of its superiority consists mainly in the fact that essences, or definitions expressing them, give us timeless relationships between qualities or between substances and their attributes. The definition may be based upon empirical observations, as in Bacon's example, but knowing the nature of heat in the Baconian sense is not what enables men to design efficient smelting furnaces, calculate the surface temperature of Jupiter, harness the sun's heat, and perform similar tasks. Although a Baconian definition may give us knowledge no less certain than our knowledge of quantitative laws, it is a knowledge we can do fewer things with. It is not the kind of knowledge that helps man reduce the element of surprise from his physical surroundings—a deep concern in our civilization since the Renaissance. For that purpose it proves necessary to introduce factors of time, force, and distance into natural knowledge, along with the measuring scales that make calculating possible. To judge the post-Baconian quantitative approach as superior is thus merely to remark that it was designed to do more than the Baconian and that it accomplishes what it was designed for.

§15 Descartes' Conception of Method

An early form of the quantitative approach found expression in the *Discourse on Method* and the unfinished *Le Monde* by René Descartes (1596–1650), the French philosopher and mathematician. In the former work Descartes expresses a concern with "learning what is new" in contrast to a syllogistic analysis of pre-existent knowledge. To further this new concern Descartes recommends four maxims:

1. Avoid prejudice; accept no proposition which is not clearly recognized to be true.
2. Divide every problem into as many subordinate ones as possible.
3. Begin the inquiry by settling the simplest questions, and advance by degrees to the more complex.
4. Review the completed inquiry to be sure nothing was omitted.[8]

[8]*Discourse on Method*, Part II.

These maxims are general enough to win approval on all sides. The decisive break with earlier conceptions of scientific method finds expression in the Cartesian doctrine that the essential properties of natural objects are identical with those of spatial extension as it is conceived in geometry. Assuming this doctrine and assuming also that men can get hold of the true first principles, should it not be possible to solve all questions step by step using geometrical proofs?

For example, in *Le Monde* Descartes claims to deduce some laws of nature from the accepted truth that an all-powerful, immutable deity exists. The constancy of the supreme being, he reasons, assures us that He acts always in the same way. From this constancy three laws are said to follow:

1. Each particle of matter remains in its own shape and in uniform motion or rest, unless changed by contact with other matter.
2. When one body moves another the mover loses as much motion as it imparts to the moved.
3. Every particle in motion tends to follow a straight path.

At one point Descartes was of the opinion that any questions of fact, even those relating to the causes and cures of disease, would one day yield to his geometrical method. Elsewhere in *Le Monde* he develops an elaborate cosmogony together with theories of heat, light, and gravity, all of which would hold true, he believed, not only for this world but for any possible one in which the Creator set matter in motion.

However, only so much of generalized physics can be made to follow from the assumption of uniformity in nature or constancy in its Creator. Consequently, Descartes discovered quite early that his geometrical method must give way to experience and experimentation where questions of fact are at issue. Descartes ran innumerable experiments in such fields as optics, anatomy, and meteorology. His account of method, however, is primarily devoted to nonempirical reasonings. In this respect it ends where recent methodological analyses begin and leaves questions about empirical reasonings to the good sense of the investigator.

Descartes' three laws of nature presage another form of the quantitative approach in science, a form that was already making strides in the work of Kepler and Galileo. That is, they are vaguely quantitative laws, although they are not yet expressed in mathematical terms. They hint at the possibility of using measurements, equations, and other arithmetical devices in physical science and of reducing sharply the element of surprise in nature. This concern, clearly expressed in the sixth part of the *Discourse* and always a factor in Descartes' total outlook, accents human needs and opposes itself to the tradition that from ancient times had revered knowledge for its own sake. Desiring knowledge of objects "to direct them to our use," as Descartes put it, does not suffice to define practicable methods or to teach men modes of finding out, but it does reveal a climate of thought friendly toward the evolution of successful methods.

§16 Mill's Methods

The English philosopher and logician John Stuart Mill (1806–1873) sought to develop a more sophisticated and flexible paradigm of method than Bacon's. Whereas the latter prescribes a way of investigating the nature of qualities such as heat and color, Mill's paradigm is designed for discovering causal relationships. Its fundamentally enumerative character, however, marks it as a first cousin of the Baconian effort. In *A System of Logic* (1848) Mill prescribes four principles to be employed in isolating the cause of a phenomenon. The first, called the Method of Agreement, he sums up in these words:

> If two or more instances of the phenomenon under investigation have only one circumstance in common, the circumstance in which alone all the instances agree is the cause. . . .[9]

It is not difficult to think of inquiries that satisfy this description. When a physician, for example, sets out to find the cause of an outbreak of food poisoning and discovers that every one of the victims attended a banquet the day before, he has found what Mill called an "agreement." Subsequent analysis of the banquet menu, narrowing the range of suspected dishes, will normally lead him to more particular agreements and before long to an identification of the tainted food.

What Mill calls his Method of Difference is expressed in this principle:

> If an instance in which the phenomenon under investigation occurs, and an instance in which it does not occur, have every circumstance in common save one, that one occurring only in the former; the circumstance in which alone the two instances differ is the cause or an indispensable part of the cause of the phenomenon.[10]

This principle, too, has clear application to examples such as our last. If it turns out that those who escaped poisoning shared everything the victims ate and drank except a salad dressing, the salad dressing is the most likely cause.

[9] *A System of Logic*, p. 280.
[10] *Loc. cit.*

Combining these rules, Mill comes up with a Joint Method of Agreement and Difference:

> If two or more instances in which the phenomenon occurs have only one circumstance in common, while two or more instances in which it does not occur have nothing in common save the absence of that circumstance, the circumstance in which alone the two sets of instances differ is the effect, or the cause, or an indispensable part of the cause, of the phenomenon.[11]

This pairing of steps corresponds in our example to the physician's noticing a factor present in all the positive instances and absent in all the negative, and in his fixing upon that factor as his prime suspect.

A fourth principle of inquiry, called the Method of Concomitant Variation, considerably widens the range of inquiries open to Mill's method:

> Whatever phenomenon varies in any manner whenever another phenomenon varies in some particular manner, is either a cause or an effect of that phenomenon, or is connected with it through some fact of causation.[12]

To illustrate this principle we may turn to an example involving recurrence and degree. The physician is now confronted with a case of allergy. The patient complains of irritated eyes and sinuses, the symptoms varying unpredictably from day to day, with seasonal relief in winter and maximum severity in summer and fall. The physician suspects pollen-sensitivity and checks the variation in symptoms against the daily pollen count. A consistent correlation will serve to confirm the diagnosis.

Expressed in the briefest possible way, Mill's principles tell us:

1. The cause of a phenomenon is something common to all the instances.
2. Anything found in negative as well as positive instances is not the cause.
3. Anything that varies proportionally with a given phenomenon is causally connected with it.

On looking back over Mill's account, it becomes clear that he offers not a condensed formulary for the actual conduct of causal inquiries but rather a highly general definition of 'cause.' Mill's definition is directed toward discovery in a way that is not true of Hume's three-part definition mentioned in the previous chapter, but it will not serve as a totally sufficient guide to discovery. Knowing in a general way the meaning of the word 'cause' is not enough to put someone on the track of a particular cause. In our example of the allergy, Mill's principles would not tell the physician that the man is suffering from allergy

11*Op. cit.*, p. 284.
12*Ibid.*, p. 287.

rather than, say, a chronic infection. Training and auxiliary knowledge are required for the diagnosis and for the knowledge of what to do next. To take a famous example, recall Henri Bequerel's noticing the peculiar effects of pitchblende on a covered photographic plate. What could cause a dark and supposedly inert substance to act on a photo-sensitive surface? Here Mill's principles might be invoked as a reminder to look for something constant or covariant, but they would not show the researcher how to look for it or what steps he must take to isolate the mysterious source of radiations. Only training in chemical analysis can do that. In a word, Mill's paradigm of method diagrams a compara-tively simple kind of causal investigation in which the cause may be found merely by inspecting instances. More complicated research proce-dures are not covered by the paradigm.

Since Mill's day, methodological studies include occasional fresh at-tempts to capture the essence of scientific procedure in a handful of general rules. By and large, however, the main concern of methodology in the twentieth century has been to analyze records of actual scientific investigations. Such records often provide detailed accounts of 'how to go about it' that are relevant to methodology but missing from the condensed and diagrammatic patterns of inductive reasoning commonly found in books of logic.

5

The Nature
and Limits
of Scientific
Truth

§17 Truth and Socratic Ignorance

Logicians of every period have remarked that their study is concerned with the pursuit of truth. Logic, that is, deals primarily with truth-functional discourse and the norms of its proper management in reasoning. In the preceding discussion of methods we have accordingly taken for granted that truth is the plain and sufficient goal of scientific inquiry. However, the concept of truth tends to generate at least as much puzzlement as any of those concepts we have considered. Philosophers and semanticists from ancient times have sought after an elusive element common to all true propositions, for instance 'agreement with reality'. Just as often they have tried to distinguish various kinds of truth-claim, noticing, for example, that some are self-evident whereas others need evidence or proof. The concepts 'true' and 'false', some have suggested, apply one way to propositions from an axiom-set in geometry but apply differently to other propositions appearing as theorems; still other differences stand out if we bring in examples from the natural sciences.

The inventory and the analysis of such differences are matters for the semanticist. Our methodological concern engages wider questions. First, what are the characteristic features of those truths that men approach through the methods of natural science? Second, what is the relationship between scientific methods and truth-claims whose features are unlike those of scientific truths? Finally, what can these distinctions teach us concerning the place of scientific truth in the broader context of human life?

Discussions and examples in earlier chapters offered a partial characterization of truths approachable through scientific methods. They are first of all truths accessible in principle to the whole interested public, so that theoretically anyone can discover them, although at the same time training, effort, and sometimes genius may be needed to find them out. Happily, they are also truths that one or a few specialized individuals can discover and publish for everyone else. They do not have to be re-established for each generation or by each new researcher. The record of research procedures employed in showing that *Aedes aegypti* transmits yellow fever is a sufficient guaranty of the truth of that proposition for any later inquirer.

A second characteristic of scientific truth is connected with the manner in which it goes out from its discoverer to the rest of the world. A typical theorist or researcher prefaces his published findings with the phrase 'to whom it may concern'. He need not use precisely those words, but their sense is conveyed when, for example, he sends his results to a learned journal, perhaps in a symbolism only his peers will understand. Even if his find is headline news, such as the discovery of Pluto a few decades ago, he will be the last to imagine that it will concern everybody. For each person who is stirred to read beyond the headline, there are ten who will turn to greater or lesser matters and leave the science news to others. The same holds true even for discoveries that pertain directly to the human race, such as artifacts and skulls attesting the great antiquity of mankind. These may excite a great many imaginations, but they do not pertain to the individual in such a way that someone's lack of interest in them bespeaks a fault in his character. A scientific truth about the human species may be psychologically startling when it first appears, but it can contain nothing personal, although it may tell him something new about his human essence, his common inheritance. For example, the discovery that manlike beings carrying clubs roamed the African veldt a million years ago has no necessary effect on one's own life and its problems.

The next characteristic of scientific truths concerns their mode of existence once they have been established. It is a passive mode. A truth of science, in other words, fulfills its role to perfection merely by being available on library shelves for anyone who happens to become concerned about it. Perhaps the researcher hopes in his heart that his discovery will be useful to physicians, engineers, and other groups who find applications for new discoveries, but meanwhile it simply stands on call, and it performs its office in that way even if it remains unread forever. A pure researcher who printed his findings and thrust them under people's noses would be thought a boor, since those who left him alone to pursue his own concerns would be denied the same courtesy.

Just as a scientific truth need not arouse anyone's notice in order to play its part in human life, so it is with the discoverer's identity. What matters is the availability of the newfound truth, not the identity of the finder. He might have been anyone with the necessary time, interest, and talent. A man of science who sees his work in this light creates an entirely satisfactory monument to himself when he places the work on file for interested members of the population. If the scientific world thanks him in perpetuity by calling it "Smith's Theory," it is with the understanding that except for an accident of circumstance, it might as easily have been named for his predecessor or his replacement.

One last characteristic of scientific truth will suffice. A truth in the scientific sphere has no voice or authority to speak to men on any matter save its own content. More particularly, a truth of science cannot properly address someone by name, scold, accuse, or do anything else that humans do to one another by using statements. This characteristic has some importance in limiting the sphere of those truths to which scientific methods are adapted.

In summary, a scientific truth belongs to a type that one man or a few can discover and pass on to others. The truth goes forth 'to whom it may concern' from discoverers who have no way of knowing the identity of those, if any, who will be concerned. As a bit of objective truth, it carries no stamp of its finder's identity, since it is not about him as an individual, although out of generosity the world may affix his name to it. It says nothing personal to or about the individual who comes upon it afterward, since it is not about him either, even when it is a truth about his species. Finally, its primary importance is to stand available, whether many or few or none ever look it up.

We hardly need to be reminded that truth-claims of a markedly different nature exist. The simplest kind to begin with might be a letter, telegram, or phone call telling someone that a loved one needs help. The statements in such a communication are just as truth-functional as any in science, but their purpose is not to go quietly on file for someone who might become concerned in the future. Instead they are meant to produce or awaken concern in a particular addressee and to pitch *him* into a crisis of decision. In this respect they make claims upon the addressee with a directness that the most glorious breakthrough in space-metallurgy or preventive medicine cannot match. Daily life is a more than adequate reminder of the existence of such truths, which for convenience we may call "unsystematic" truths, since they have no place in any organized body of knowledge.

The concept of truth relates to still another class of propositions that may be described in general as truths about the individual existing man. We can call these "Socratic" truths after the Greek philosopher Socrates, whose life expressed a classic concern for them in the fifth century B.C. Socrates' mission, as he recounts it in Plato's *Apology,* was to approach the citizens of Athens singly and to remind them of the importance and also of the elusiveness of the kind of truth that reveals a person to himself. Socratic truth divides into two types, each related to the existing man in a distinct way. The first type consists of truths that he carries within himself and that find expression in his treatment of himself and of others. These include what he really thinks of himself and of his human existence. Does he think it a trifle, a matter of indifference? Does he regard it as significant for eternity? Would he prefer not to declare an opinion? *What* he thinks is by definition uncertain, since he *thinks* it is so, and it may in the last analysis prove false. However, the fact that he does think such and such about himself and his existence is itself a truth about him. For example, it is not a Socratic truth that many American Negroes have been cruelly deprived of their rights; it is a historical truth documented in works of social science. However, if I can do something about it but refuse, this fact about myself is a clue to a Socratic truth, namely, that I do not think a human in trouble is worth inconveniencing myself for. This in turn hints at what I really think of my own humanity, the mere man underneath those extras that good fortune may have heaped upon me. This truth about what I really think, like the truths of science, is true regardless of anyone else's opinion; unlike truths of science, however, it cannot be discovered and passed on to me by another. Also unlike science, its status as truth is very closely bound up with the identity of the one who expresses it.

A second class of propositions concerned with the Socratic sphere of truth includes those that do not arise within the individual but purport to come from outside himself and to teach him about his ultimate origin, value, and future. Conflicting pronouncements in this area address the individual with various claims of authority and offer to remedy his Socratic ignorance. Christianity proclaims a divine revelation and the gift of faith; Buddhism presents itself on the testimony of a human sage. There are others as well, but our present concern does not call for an airing of opposed truth-claims or for a judgment of validity. Instead we are out to discern a boundary beyond which the methods of natural science do not work; by doing that, we may hope to view from another side the area in which they work supremely well.

§18 The Neutrality of Scientific Truth

Science advances no claims concerning Socratic issues. The methods of science are adapted to establishing the kind of truth that relates only accidentally to a particular existing man, usually because of a special interest that he happens to have. A few thinkers have tried to employ experimental methods directly in the Socratic areas, for example by rigging apparatuses to register voices and other phenomena they associate with a spirit world. Unambiguous results would presumably settle the general question about surviving death, although it is hard to see how they would do much for the Socratic question about the inquirer's own survival. In any event, no positive results from spiritualistic experiments have won over the scientific community.

Of the two types of Socratic truth we have described, the former clearly has no connection with scientific methods. It is not found out or discovered in any ordinary sense of those terms but rather is brought to light by being given expression in the individual's decisions and deeds, including verbal ones. If a man in moments of self-searching wishes to ask what *he* thinks his existence comes to or what, if anything, he really thinks is serious in it, a book of science is the last place he would look for answers.

However, when we turn back to Socratic concerns of the second kind, those touching the meaning of existence and the individual's place in it, we find that not all thinkers agree with Socrates in calling science neutral. There is general agreement that experimental methods cannot be directly applied to solving these concerns, but many writers feel that the accumulated findings of modern science offer some important leads. Science, the argument goes, has been so much expanded since its origins in ancient thought that it can be consulted on the deepest questions of life. Unfortunately, this belief in the virtually unlimited reach of scientific methods has produced a great deal of mischief and distraction. In order to see more clearly where the authority of science ends, it will be useful to examine a few representative claims put forward in recent times by popularizers of science. These claims tend to group around three so-called "revolutions" in the history of science associated with the rise of modern astronomy, evolutionary theory, and psychoanalysis. These advances are frequently said to have caused basic reversals in Western man's conception of himself.

Since Galileo's day, especially in our age of great telescopes, men have grown accustomed to speaking of unnumbered island universes, millions or billions of light-years, and a cosmos of increasing and indeterminable immensity. The closed sphere of ancient cosmologies with its fixed stars hanging equidistant from a central earth is unthinkable today. There are at least 100 billion stars in the single galactic system to which our sun belongs. Millions of systems similar to the Milky Way dot the heavens, ranging indefinitely far out from the nearest one, which is 150,000 light-years distant. The human who asks "Where am I?" and looks about for a cosmic map will find none with absolute co-ordinates.

He is on a planet going around a star on the fringe of a star system whose diameter a beam of light would take more than 200,000 years to cross, a system not privileged to call itself more central than any other. In the classical period of Greece and for many centuries thereafter, the question "Where am I?" was answered by reference to earth as the center of celestial motions.

From the belief that this planet is the hub of the universe, an individual can derive no cogent answers to Socratic questions about his origin or the value of his existence. However, many recent thinkers have suggested that the new astronomy offers answers to those questions. One philosopher of science writes:

> ... Man's mother earth is but a speck in the boundlessness of space, his place even on earth but insignificant and precarious; in a word, he is at the mercy of brute forces that unknowingly happened to throw him into being, and promise ere long just as unknowingly to snuff out the candle of his little day. Himself and all that is dear to him will in course of time become "buried in a universe of ruins."
>
> This is, of course, an extreme position; at the same time is it not true that the reflective modern man, in his cosmological moods, feels this analysis of the situation thrusting itself upon him with increasing cogency?[1]

If the cogency of Burtt's analysis is not increasing, at any rate repetitions of it are; one can hardly find a popular author on astronomy in the last decade who does not glance wistfully back toward the orderly universe of Dante and then express a resolve not to accept such comfort. A little later in his book Burtt speaks of

> ... the pathetic characteristic of human nature which enables man easily to think more highly of himself than he ought to think—to swallow gullibly a flattering notion of his own importance in the drama of the ages. . . .[2]

From quotations of the sort just given it would appear that the findings of modern astronomy and allied sciences put us well on the way to a new cure for Socratic ignorance, a cure not available to the ancients. The cure may be summed up in the idea that, in a universe as stupendous as this one, to be unknowingly thrown into being as a particular human is probably no very serious matter and almost certainly not serious for eternity. However, in order to be quite sure that the Socratic issues here have been settled by reference to scientific findings and not just evaded, it will repay Burtt's reader to inspect very closely the method by which he moves from the unquestioned data of astronomy to the conclusions in his analysis. A closer look reveals no logical connection at

[1]E. A. Burtt, *The Metaphysical Foundations of Modern Science* (New York: Humanities Press, 1954), p. 24.
[2]*Ibid.*, p. 26.

all between them. The conclusions do not follow either as necessary inferences, as probabilities, or as presumptive likelihoods. The world-picture presented by astronomy is simply uninformative on Socratic issues of the second type. Burtt's analysis develops only when a human being looks at that world-picture, feels understandably dwarfed by its dimensions, and allows that feeling to color his attitude toward Socratic questions. This feeling can make it look as though the full authority of modern science stands behind Burtt's analysis, whereas what has occurred is a psychological reaction of awe and melancholy, not a piece of reasoning.

The illusion that clues from science promise a cure for Socratic ignorance arises in part from the notion that science is some kind of enormously erudite and thoughtful personality or spirit, whose deliverances can teach man his place and humble him much in the way that the God of Scripture calls him a sinner, a creature of the dust. Thus another astronomer writes:

> . . . 'What is the meaning and object of it all?' This is the question that down the ages has puzzled all the thinkers and all the philosophers without any real satisfactory answer being found. And now it seems only Science is left to appeal to, and what science says is that there is no indication whatsoever in the whole cosmos that there is any discernible purpose at all.[3]

Unlike a deity, however, science does not possess a consciousness or a voice independent of the human voices that articulate it. When science speaks, man and nothing else speaks. Approached as a confidante in Socratic matters, science can therefore reply only by ventriloquism. The stage ventriloquist, in contrast, presents a harmless amusement as he sustains the illusion that his dummy is doing the talking. If we suppose a far more towering man-made construction and men earnestly seeking its counsel on the deepest questions, we are no longer discussing the category of entertainment.

Is this to say that astronomy can teach us nothing at all relevant to Socratic issues? By no means. It may be useful for men to command a realistic view of the physical setting in which they raise their Socratic questions, to be aware, for example, that the world is not a distractingly fantastic dish borne on the back of a colossal tortoise, as in the Hindu legend. It is helpful and relevant to know there are men who specialize in separating fact from fancy as regards the shape of the earth and the size of the universe. On the other hand, where astronomy offers no inference from its data to the individual's own life-condition, but only a sober and accurate description of the gross setting of his life, he can be grateful for that description without deifying its source.

[3]Raymond A. Lyttleton, *The Modern Universe* (New York: Harper & Brothers, 1956), pp. 205–6.

§19   A Confusion of the Spheres

When the border between scientific and Socratic concerns is wholly ignored, confusion follows. The individual's real debt to science, in our civilization a considerable one in terms of both knowledge and comfort, goes out of clear focus, and likewise his debt to himself as an existing man. Keeping the spheres distinct is a task requiring no special intelligence, since many average people manage to do it and quite a few men of commanding intellect fail. Yet it does require a certain balance in the mind between scientific knowledge and self-knowledge, a balance not always to be found in those who are fully taken up with the wealth and interest of a science. Some further examples may help to illustrate this kind of imbalance.

A second upheaval in Western thought began in the nineteenth century when Darwin's theory appeared. Just as a number of thinkers had found it dispiriting to be told they were not at the physical center of the cosmos, others now expressed alarm at the idea that the human form may have dragged its way up somehow from lower animal forms through long geological periods. There is no need to repeat here our earlier references to Darwin's main ideas or to the facts that prompted him to formulate them. Instead, to illustrate the confusion of spheres it will be useful to notice a particular way of speaking that made its appearance in Darwin's lifetime and has colored discussion down to the present day:

> ... The hypotheses respecting the origin of species which profess to stand upon a scientific basis, and, as such, alone demand serious attention, are of two kinds. The one, the 'special creation' hypothesis, presumes every species to have originated from one or more stocks, these not being the result of modification of any other form of living matter—but being produced, as such, by a supernatural creative act. The other, the so-called 'transmutation' hypothesis, considers that all existing species are the result of the modification of pre-existing species, and those of their predecessors, by agencies similar to those which at the present day produce variations and races, and therefore in an altogether natural way. . . .[4]

In this and other passages Thomas Huxley applies the term 'hypothesis' to the biblical account of creation as found for example in Genesis 1, 21:

> And God created the great whales, and every living and moving creature, which the waters brought forth, according to their kinds, and every winged fowl according to its kind.

Popular writers on evolution have copied Huxley's usage until it has come to sound as safe as any in the language. If there is any misunder-

[4]Thomas H. Huxley, *Selected Works* (New York and London: D. Appleton & Co., 1893) . Vol. II, *Darwiniana*, pp. 53–54.

standing involved in calling the idea of creation a hypothesis, Darwinians are not alone to blame; attacked as a bad hypothesis, it has also been defended as a blessed one. Some of its defenders have described it as a primitive hypothesis, tinged with fancy, in which an ancient people tried to explain in its own terms the origin of living things.

To call something a hypothesis (moreover, one professing to stand upon a scientific basis) is to attribute to it a number of characteristics that we reviewed back in Chapter 3. If the idea of creation possesses those characteristics, there is no impropriety in calling it a hypothesis. If not, then whether the idea of creation is true or false in any eternal reckoning, we can ask if Huxley's usage is misleading in a way that confuses the scientific and Socratic spheres.

A truth-claim removed from the circumstances of its use does not wear any sure indicator that it functions as a hypothesis. To get clear about its role we must examine it in its natural habitat to see if it exhibits the normal characteristics of hypotheses. With this aim in mind let us compare two statements:

A.   Whales evolved from land-mammals.
B.   God created the great whales.

As noted before, a hypothesis has for its basic purpose the explanation of a puzzling fact. Sentence A has been used to help explain why certain species of whale possess rudimentary hind legs buried in their blubber and why they possess a set of teeth that never erupt through the gum and never function to chew anything (see *The Origin of Species*, Chap. XIV). That is, if whales had evolved from land-mammals and if certain organs are likely to atrophy when a land-species becomes aquatic, what could be more natural than to find useless teeth and residual limbs in modern whales?

Now sentence B may also be regarded as answering a possible question, such as "What accounts for the existence of whales?" However, even if B were ever seriously used for that purpose, this would not suffice to give B the full character of a hypothesis. Hypotheses, we may recall, are not only answers to possible puzzlers but are suggested by knowledge of the physical surroundings of the phenomenon to be explained. Clues in the anatomy of whales, taken together with a general picture of natural processes, suggest that A may be true. B, on the other hand, no matter what its actual origin may have been, did not come into the world as an inference from details of the whale's anatomy. There are no biological clues hinting that whales were wished into existence by a god, nor is there any agreement among biologists as to what such clues would look like.

This reasoning begins to separate statements A and B; to distinguish them further, we turn next to the way they explain facts. Statement A explains residual nonfunctioning organs by referring us to some proximate physical conditions that might account for them. The creation statement, on the other hand, brings in the name of God. In no way does it adduce any physical circumstances to account for the existence of whales, again assuming it were actually used for that purpose. Further, B has no experimental consequences that, if followed up, would tend to confirm biologists in the view that whales were indeed wished into being by a deity. With A in mind, however, biologists can hope to find other rudimentary organs in living species and perhaps fossil remains of transitional stages in the whale's evolution.

It would appear from this comparison that the idea of creation, whatever one might want to say about it on other grounds, neither originates nor functions in the manner of a scientific hypothesis. The contrast between A and B has led many authors, including Huxley, to set aside the idea of creation as a third-rate and outworn hypothesis. Once we accept Huxley's usage and call creation a hypothesis to begin with, it can of course be nothing but a bad one, easily the world's worst explanation of whales' hind legs. We are under no initial obligation, however, to regard it as a hypothesis. The tendency, now routine, to call it by that name arises from a failure to distinguish scientific from Socratic truth-claims. To re-establish the boundary in terms of this example, it will be useful to contrast the two ideas, evolution and creation, in a little more depth.

We should not be diverted by the fact that some statements in which the idea of creation appears read like plain cosmogony, biology, or natural history. Unfortunately, the fact that the logic may sound the same in scientific and in Scriptural texts can obscure the kind of distinction that must be kept in mind if the spheres are not to blur together. The truth-claim in Genesis that God created whales occurs in a chapter whose primary purpose is to inform the *reader* that he is a *creature*. It claims, in other words, to add one determinant to the reader's personal knowledge of himself as a particular existing man, by telling him that he exists in relation to a God and that he is the object of a creator's notice, love, wrath, or whatever might be disclosed in reading further. In thus addressing itself to the reader personally and in claiming to tell him something about himself that none of his scientific brethren could discover and pass along to him, Genesis falls into the category of Socratic rather than scientific truth-claims. There is no method, at any rate none among those we have discussed, by which an individual could establish experimentally that he stands in the relation "creature of" to a hidden God. One may accept such a claim or scoff at it. However, to call it a hypothesis and then call it a bad one is to use an extremely misleading form of the latter response, in the sense that it fails to acknowledge the personal reference to the reader.

Along with the idea of creation in Genesis is the related idea that the Creator knows his reader personally and that the reader has no secrets from the Creator. Accordingly, the sentences in Genesis, that have 'whales' and 'fowl' as their grammatical subjects claim to be addressing an understood subject, the reader himself in his creaturehood. This is what we stated earlier the sentences of science never do: speak to men in the manner of an independent voice or speak about the reader's personal existence. Some further contrasts will reinforce this difference between scientific and Socratic, but for the moment we may remind ourselves that the scientist, even when his subject is man, clearly does not claim to know his reader personally; if his sentences have any understood subject, it is not "you" but "whoever happens to be concerned."

Here someone might readily protest that the border between scientific and Socratic concerns need not be regarded as a *sealed* border. It is true that the line between them can be crossed at many points without becoming blurred or forgotten. The Socratic meditations of many individuals have been enriched by the lore of maturing sciences. Our concern is not to assert a doctrine of two inconsistent kinds of truth but merely to notice how easily truth-claims in Socratic areas can be obscured.

By reading Socratic truth-claims as if they were scientific ones, as we just saw, a thinker can screen out of consciousness the real burden and target of the Socratic claims. On the other hand, by reading scientific truth-claims as if they were Socratic, as in the example dealing with modern astronomy, he can transform the results of empirical research into a dummy that repeats his own sentiments back to him. A fairly common type of transformation along these lines may be found in writers who popularize evolutionary biology. It proceeds by borrowing a diction and a tone appropriate to personal communications but applying them in a purely scientific context. An example from the pen of Mr. Julian Huxley, who is not only a popular author but a distinguished scientist, shows some of the comic dissonances that can result when the spheres are muddled:

> ...You, like me and every other human being, were once a microscopic spherical ovum, then in turn a double sheet of undifferentiated cells, an embryo with enormous outgrowths enabling you to obtain food and oxygen parasitically from your mother, a creature with an unjointed rod—what biologists call the notochord—in place of a jointed backbone; you once had

a tail, and once were covered with dense hair like a monkey; you were once a helpless infant which had to learn to distinguish objects and to talk; you underwent the transformation of your body and mind that we call puberty; you learnt a job. You are in fact a self-transforming process.[5]

The purely scientific foundation for these remarks, their factual points of reference, came to light when naturalists sought to explain non-functional human organs such as the vermiform appendix, certain features of human embryology, and structural resemblances to lower animal forms. Those characteristics are most conveniently explained by supposing a genetic link between modern man and distant forebears. However, Huxley's recital of man's animal attributes is tuned an octave higher than the moderate tone of a textbook in human biology. The driving rhythm, the repetition of the personal pronoun "you," and the use of faintly opprobrious expressions such as "like a monkey" together suggest the atmosphere of a tribunal where the accused listens to a reading of his police file, wondering whether he can ever hold his head up again after a public charge of behaving like a parasite toward his own mother. The references to human animality in this passage are saved from impertinence by the fact that they apply equally to every human, not to the reader singled out as a particular "you." However, any blame for the improbable tone of the passage must go to its author, not to the science he practices. A magisterial, finger-pointing tone is something only we humans can affect. By speaking in that register one person seeks to create in another a state of mindfulness where there was none before, but the propositions of science have no mind of their own that could conceive such an intention. Scientific truth gets much of its dignity from the fact that all personal byplay has been systematically scrubbed from the methods employed in reaching it and from the language employed in expressing it.

Our examples thus far have called attention to relatively simple confusions between the scientific and Socratic spheres of human concern. The pure data of astronomy can tempt a thinker to draw or imagine he draws inferences of a non-astronomical kind. The richer theoretical content of evolutionary biology, with its direct references to man, can occasion confusion in two ways, either by leading someone to read Socratic truth-claims as if they were scientific or by leading him to read scientific truth-claims as if they were Socratic. For a closing example of greater complexity, we turn to a portion of psychoanalytic theory as developed by Sigmund Freud.

Psychoanalytic techniques for the relief of hysteria and of neuroses were created in large part by Freud, who labored until his death in 1939

[5] Julian Huxley, *Evolution in Action* (New York: Harper & Brothers, 1953), pp. 16–17.

in the double capacity of therapist and theorist. The theory that he brought into being along with his clinical procedures deals with almost every aspect of human life.[6] Although some portions of it are less finished than others, the theory proposes a total view of human nature. Its general aim is to chart the forces that interplay in the human psyche, much as an oceanographer seeks to chart the rivers of water that move in various depths of the sea. Freud sought to explain minor mental phenomena such as slips of the tongue as well as the major forms of mental distress. In addition his theory treats of phenomena well within the normal range, for instance, dreams, the choice of a career, and the practice of one's religion.

Not a believer himself, Freud professed a strong interest in the religious behavior of others. One of his most persistent and heartfelt aims, according to biographers, was to explain how it happens that many persons believe in a God and try to manage their lives in the light of that belief. Although Freud occasionally displays learning in connection with other religions, for instance, the Egyptian monotheism of Ikhnaton, his main concern in this area of the theory is the Judaeo-Christian religious tradition. With that in mind he asks: How could the essential idea of God in that tradition have arisen and taken hold of people's minds?

If Freud had tried to answer this question by asking believers why they believe, they would doubtless have referred him to an abiding tradition of temple, church, and Scripture in which the commands and permissions of the God they believe in are assumed to be set down. Freud, however, forbade himself to allow that a God could have had anything to do with the origins of Jewish and Christian beliefs. On the surface, at least, this is merely good scientific practice; as we saw earlier, bringing in the name of the Almighty to account for a puzzling phenomenon would go against the rules of sound theory-construction in the sciences. To this methodological maxim, however, Freud gave a special twist which violates the neutrality of science in relation to Socratic truth-claims. That is, instead of just omitting any reference to a divine power in his efforts at scientific explanation, Freud permitted himself to assume that no God exists and hence that religious behavior in other people represents a species of illusion. The difference here is between legitimately keeping the name of God out of scientific theories, on the one hand, and on the other, postulating the nonexistence of God as *part of the theory*.

[6]For an ample account of the development of Freud's doctrines see Ernest Jones, *The Life and Work of Sigmund Freud*, 3 vols. (New York: Basic Books, 1957). A more balanced estimate of Freud's contribution can be found in Karl Stern, *The Third Revolution* (New York: Doubleday Image series, 1961).

Firmly committed to this methodological misunderstanding, Freud plunged ahead in his attempts to explain belief in God. There must be some psychological need underlying worship that forms a visible element in the lives of other people. What need could that be? Perhaps worship appeases guilt-feelings, he conjectured. Yet many of these people have not done very much to feel guilty about. Then perhaps it is not their personal guilt that plagues them, but a kind of guilt-inheritance, the traces of events that happened long ago in history and were momentous enough to leave a permanent and inheritable crease on the unconscious minds of later generations. These remote and mysterious events, Freud suggested, may have been murders of tribal chiefs. Believers accept one God rather than many because the chiefs of old were monarchs, and they insist on an invisible God because invisibility signifies the primacy of intellect over senses.

It is not especially useful to hunt for bits of illogic in this strange theory, nor does the average lay reader of Freud's work possess the specialized learning needed to challenge it on psychological or historical details. However, it is useful and important to show that Freud's and similar theories involve a serious confusion of the scientific and the Socratic spheres and that a brilliant and inventive scientist can be just as vulnerable to that kind of confusion as his most plodding disciple.

Further examination of Freud's theoretical approach tends to uncover a misunderstanding somewhat more fundamental than the one already noted. This second misunderstanding consists in the assumption that a scientific theory can bear decisively upon the individual's relationship to Socratic truth-claims of the second kind. The theorist in this instance takes for granted from the start that he has access to the innermost being of other persons and that by the power of his thought *qua* scientist he is in a position to pronounce their relationship to such truth-claims either well founded or illusory. He begins by noticing a large class of phenomena in their lives, such as praying, studying the Scriptures, reciting creeds, observing feasts and fasts, foregathering at designated places, and many more. The origins and psychological significance of these practices, he feels, ought to be explained in a scientific theory, a task he undertakes himself. What then will be the role of the resulting theory in the intellectual lives of the theorist himself and of believers who later run across it?

As regards the theorist himself, his theory appears at first to raise him to a height far above other humans, a pinnacle from which he can discern the illusions of those others. That would indeed be a valuable extra benefit of a theory. However, to assure ourselves that this heightened vision is exactly what it first seems and not something of an illusion in its own right, we must next inquire what it is that Freud calls an illusion and by what method he arrives at his judgment. On the first point, what Freud calls an illusion is the relationship between the believer and the God he believes in. The believer's prayers and observances are all for the sake of that relationship, its sustenance and renewal. What method, then, guides Freud to the judgment that the relationship is an illusion? Here we find no determinate method open to the theorist. He cannot, for example, inspect the relationship directly, as a lineman might test a telephone connection. He cannot show that Smith's relationship to a God is unreal in comparison with Brown's real one, which would itself be an unpublic relationship between Brown and a hidden God. The only way to reach a scientific verdict concerning someone else's relationship to a God is to assume the verdict at the outset, and that is exactly what Freud does. Despite first appearances, then, the theory fails to enlarge its author's understanding of its subject, the nature of religious belief in Judaism and Christianity. Yet that expansion of understanding is supposed to be the function of a theory.

The role of the theory in the intellectual life of a believer who chances upon it is similarly deceptive in its startling first effects. At first it seems to deliver an extraordinary piece of news concerning himself as a believer, namely, that for some time he has been caught up in an illusion. Thus the theory can threaten to come between the person and his religious beliefs. On further investigation, however, the threat virtually disappears.

To illustrate, let us imagine an educated man who counts himself a believer and also cherishes a profound respect for science, not only as a provider of better things for better living, but even more as a record of human intellectual achievement. Then he comes across Freud's theory, which speaks of his relationship to God as an illusion. "Here is a carefully worked-out scientific theory," his opening thoughts might run, "and if there is anything faulty in it I am hardly enough of an expert to argue with the scientist who constructed it. I could pretend I had never heard of this disturbing theory, but I have too much respect for theories to do that. At the same time, though, I am certainly reluctant to attach myself to anything that has been labeled 'illusion' by a scientific titan."

But a serious person will not stop here. When his second thoughts have had a chance to form themselves he may continue, "How, I wonder, did this theorist work himself into a position from which he could inspect my relationship to God? If, for example, I had believed myself to be in another sort of relationship, for instance, mayor of the Emerald City of Oz, and had been trying to live in consciousness of that relationship, I could understand why a theorist would shake his head. The emerald towers would be suspiciously absent from his field of vision. God, on the other hand, is indeed nowhere to be seen with the eyes, but is He *suspiciously* absent? He would be that only if He were the kind of being man or nature puts together, which could conceivably turn up as a piece of the world's furniture. But nobody imagines the God of the Testaments to be of that sort. This theory, then, has no application whatever to me or to my relationship to God. I would feel the same way if Freud had said instead that my relationship to God is as sound and as real as can be. Whether he called it real or unreal, in other words, I would still want to ask how he managed to get a look at it." By means of second thoughts along these lines the individual can recover a relaxed attitude toward scientific theories that might at first seem to have disturbing consequences in the sphere of Socratic truth-claims.

As it turns out, Freud's speculations about religious belief contribute nothing to the theorist's understanding of belief or to the believer's understanding of himself. This may seem an excessively strong and negative estimate of this part of Freud's work and may lead someone to object that his years of painstaking thought about other people's worship of God must have produced some valid insights along the way. That is not to be denied a priori, but if the opposite were true it would not be the first time a scientific effort failed by misunderstanding the individual's relation to truths in the Socratic sphere. Freud's theory of religious belief represents an extreme example of the idea that science has authority to chide or to persuade humans in that sphere, when in fact chiding is something only humans do. There are many more theories of that sort, too many for any brief survey to cover or for any single formula to rebut. The reader who trains himself to spot them can not only help keep the spheres clearly separate in his own mind, but can do so without losing any of that fundamental respect for scientific truth that is a mark of our civilization.

§20 Scientific Methods and the Knowable

Our immediate aim in this chapter has been to characterize in some detail the kind of truth-claim associated with scientific methods by contrasting it with a type of claim that exercises human minds of every generation, regardless of the level of scientific sophistication in any particular century. By dividing our domains of concern into scientific and Socratic, it is possible to exhibit the latter as a domain in which the methods of natural science, except insofar as they coincide with straight thinking in general, are of no avail. In a certain sense this division declares limits to the reach of scientific inquiry, but only in one area. In all others it should be emphasized that the methods of science are capable of extending without limit the knowledge man has amassed. This idea has found utterance in maxims such as C. S. Peirce's "Do not block the road of inquiry"—a warning against calling this or that scientific question unanswerable in principle. The maxim can be expressed positively in the dictum that man's faculties are equal to explaining whatever happens or has happened in nature, and negatively in the idea that the natural order contains no unknowables.

Like a number of other principles in the logic of science, this one would rank as a truism except that certain thinkers have taken the trouble to deny it. The difficulty, as with methodological principles generally, is to express Peirce's maxim in a manner that will show it to be grounded in something more than naïve optimism. For example, to assert that nothing in nature is absolutely unknowable is not to suggest that nature operates with a toy-like transparency. The assertion is not an observation about nature at all, but a reflection of the fact that scientific methods are so conceived as to exclude any question of giving up. What some philosophers of this century would call the "grammar" of scientific practice, meaning roughly the range of linguistic and experimental techniques that grew up as the sciences advanced, has no room in it for expressions of despair. Thus if a medical researcher were to shut down his laboratory, proclaiming that nothing causes epilepsy and nothing can ever cure it, we would see in his words a strange failure of nerve rather than a report of the latest experimental findings. To call something unknowable is to venture the dim prophecy that human wits will never exceed their present grasp of nature; but no individual is in a position to speak this way in the name of the whole scientific community.

Besides raising epistemological issues of the kinds we have been considering, the copious accumulation of scientific learning in the last few centuries has prompted men to revive ancient questions about what is worth knowing. When Aristotle remarked that all men by nature desire to know, he suspended questions about the relative importance of this or that piece of information and spoke quite generally of the delight we take in our senses and faculties. The instruments of science are extensions of our sense organs and musculature, and its methods are extensions of the discursive and graphic languages in which men pursue questions. Scientific methods are representative of a discipline purged of such human weaknesses as a limited attention span and a craving for the merely spectacular, a discipline guaranteeing that in addition to beholding interesting sights men will learn something definite. Whether the interesting as such is the highest object of man's affections is a question we must leave unanswered. However, the idea that men by nature desire knowledge means that scientific truth is pursued as a love object by numbers of persons who would protest any demand for further justification of their calling.

Index